The Rocks Remain

Ring of Bright Water, which has delighted countless thousands of readers, is one of the most famous books to have been published since the war. *The Rocks Remain* continues the story of Gavin Maxwell's life both at Camusfeàrna, his lonely cottage on the West Highland seaboard, and abroad, in North Africa and Majorca. But though a true sequel to its famous precursor, it strikes a new and, in some ways, richer note.

Ring of Bright Water described the pioneering days at Camusfeàrna with the otters Mijbil and Edal. *The Rocks Remain*, with the acquisition of new otters – Teko, Mossy, Monday and others – with the arrival of electricity at the remote cottage, with extensions to the buildings and additions to the transport facilities, with the acquisition of the motor-vessel *Polar Star*, with the author's marriage, and with the sometimes unwelcome spotlight of publicity on his private life, is a book written from deeper and wider experience.

This story of the succeeding years, though full of fresh delights, especially in its perceptive descriptions of the otters, is not without episodes of danger and even disaster. Both Edal and Teko, despite their astonishingly affectionate relationship with the author, give sudden and frightening evidence that otters cannot yet be trusted with humans other than their acknowledged foster-parents. The wreck of the *Polar Star* in which the author all but lost his life, an explosion in the kitchen at Camusfeàrna, an invasion of rats, the total and spectacular destruction in Majorca of the author's new Mercedes-Benz, are transmuted from chapters of calamity to chapters of breath-taking suspense and high comedy. The scenes in North Africa, mysterious, strange, sometimes farcical, throw into vivid focus the life at Camusfeàrna to which the author always returns as though to spring water from the desert.

The Rocks Remain is a further superbly written revelation of a personality, a place and a way of life that have captured the imagination of readers the world over.

THE
ROCKS
REMAIN

Gavin Maxwell

Longmans

LONGMANS GREEN & CO LTD
48 Grosvenor Street, London W.1
*Associated companies, branches, and representatives
throughout the world*

*Printed and bound in Great Britain
by Jarrold and Sons Ltd, Norwich*

This book is for
those who Remain my Rocks

Acknowledgements

WE ARE GRATEFUL to the following for permission to include copyright material:

John Calder Ltd. for an extract from *The Naked Lunch* by William S. Burroughs; the *New Statesman* for the poem 'The Scapegoat' by Gavin Maxwell, an earlier version of which appeared in the issue of 28 June 1952; Oxford University Press, Bombay, for an extract from *Twin Rivers* by Seton Lloyd, and Putnam & Co. Ltd. for 'The Circulation of Light' from *The Smell of Burning* by Thomas Blackburn.

The following photographs were taken by James Millar Watt: the two indoor pictures in the sequence *Edal in her new quarters*; *Edal exploring the syphon outflow to her new pool*; the picture on the sand in the sequence *Teko and Dirk*; the picture with the life-belt in the sequence *Teko's reaction to a life-belt*; *Mossy as an infant*; the sequence *Mossy during the first weeks*; the sequence *Terry and Monday on the day she arrived*; the sequence *Monday's first experiments in water*; the close-up in the sequence *Mossy and Monday* facing page 133; the sequence *Mossy and Monday: 'They had taken up permanent residence under the floor of the new wing'*; the lower picture in the sequence *Lavinia, Dirk and Monday*; the beach scene facing page 165.

We are grateful to Garage Auto-Freno, Palma, for permission to reproduce the photographs of the damaged Mercedes.

All other photographs were taken by the author.

The endpapers are by Robin McEwen.

Contents

List of Illustrations

Nicholas
Simon
The column that the Mercedes struck after her *tête à queue* at 100 m.p.h.
What remained of the Mercedes
Camusfeàrna, February 1963
The *Polar Star*, April 1963

1

Portrait of an Earthquake

To the most turbulent of lives come unforeseen periods of calm and tranquillity, as though some river running perpetually over rapids broadened suddenly into a deep, still pool of silence. Such a season of fair weather, an idyll belonging more properly to childhood or to old age, I described in *Ring of Bright Water*, the story of the West Highland cottage that I have called Camusfeàrna and of the otters that shared it with me. The time that this narrative covered represented perhaps the most placid period of my adult life; but without knowing it I had drifted nearer and nearer to the tail of the pool (for, I think, I had been in no backwater but in one of the main stream's many and various reaches), nearer to the rock lip where the water falls in cascade and spume before rushing on towards the sea. I was caught again in the full strength of a shallower current, whirled as a *bateau ivre* back into its familiar confusion, striking greater and lesser boulders as I had done before, and more closely aware of the other human beings who were swept along with me.

Thus this book, though a true sequel to its precursor, will have little of its flavour; it is the partial story of the succeeding years, their difficulties, disasters and delights; and if disaster either so minor as to be comic or so major as to appear tragic seems to predominate, it is, like the rocks that remain, in the eye of the beholder.

The title represents not so much the residuum as the remembered catalyst of a long preoccupation. I first heard the song during the early years of the war, and then it was the nostalgia of

I

the words and tune that made me consciously remember them. The words were clumsy – almost, in places, McGonagall – and I remember trying to rewrite them, trying to transmute their clichés, so that now I am uncertain whether the first verse, from which I have taken my title, is the original old Scottish version or a relic of some attempt of mine at improvement.

> Age on age the rocks remain,
> And the tides return again;
> Only we poor mourners, sinners
> Weavers, toilers, fishers, spinners,
> Pass away like visions vain.

In either case it was, as I have said, the superficial appeal of the nostalgic theme that engrossed me then, a theme recurrent in so much northern folksong. Later, I became engrossed with the image of the rock not as a single symbol of permanence but in the dual role of saviour and destroyer; the rock, in whose lee one ship may shelter from storm, will destroy another that lies to windward; the reef that forms a harbour is in itself the greatest possible peril until it has been successfully negotiated. This theme I tried to express in several poems – or rather one poem in several parts – published in the *New Statesman* not long after the war; none of them is worthy of repetition, but I quote the concluding verses with all their imperfections as at least clarifying the title of this book.

> Whatever arm can stem the sea
> Can claw the shrinking planks apart,
> The rocks that pierce the carvelled tree
> Are strong to harbour and to hurt,
> O, shield and spear unite in me.
> One with the island now my hull
> Is clenched within the creviced rock;
> One with sea when tide's at full
> She holds the power of shield and shock,
> The sheltering arm, the hidden skull.

I had never seen this theme developed in any medium until recently I saw, and acquired, a painting by Michael Ayrton, in which sombre forms possessing the quintessential qualities both of boat and of rock stood as the foreground to a ferocious yet strangely remote sea. This painting now hangs in my sitting-room at Camusfeàrna, and is the subject of much vexed speculation by the average visitor who wants to know whether these are in fact 'meant' to be rocks or boats, and exactly where the sealine is 'supposed' to join the sky.

In the same way there will no doubt be those who expected from this book a second *Ring of Bright Water* and who will want to know exactly where events abroad are 'supposed' to join those at Camusfeàrna, and whether certain incidents are 'meant' to be disastrous or farcical. Like the demarcation line between sea and sky, and like the application of realism to the boat-rocks on the shore, these questions have no relevance to my theme.

I finished the manuscript of *Ring of Bright Water* at Camusfeàrna on October 16th 1959. I was then, and at the time of writing still am, engaged upon lengthy but not always leisurely research into certain aspects of twentieth-century Moroccan history, and at about eleven-thirty on the evening of March 1st the following year I was writing in a small and exceedingly shabby room in the *medina*, or old Arab town, of Marrakesh. It was the eve of Independence Day. It was also the end of the second day of Ramadan, the annual Muslim month of fast during the daylight hours, and the near-by Place Djemma El Fna was loud with drums, tambourines, pipes, and the brass bells of water-sellers – the whole babel of a people for whom, during this season, the night becomes the only time of activity. It was a warm, breathless night, and the air was heavy with the smell of spices and cooking.

The single electric light bulb dangling from the high ceiling gave a light inadequate for writing, and I was bent low over the table. 'Hadj Abdullah ou Bihi, grand caid of the Haha', I wrote carefully, 'was sent for to the Sultan's palace, where he was given the choice of a cup of poisoned tea or starvation to death while publicly exhibited in an iron . . .' The word I was writing trailed off into a meaningless hieroglyphic. It seemed as though someone had shaken my chair violently from behind; automatically I looked over my shoulder, and as I did so a long shudder shook the room and the tiles of the floor seemed to slope towards me. My pen and some small change clattered down from the table. The house was of the flimsy construction common to most of the *medina*, and my first thought was that someone was moving heavy furniture in a contiguous part of the building. A second later the shudder was repeated, the same sensation of vibration and tilting as when a ship's screws are lifted clear of the water as she pitches in a heavy sea. The explanation of furniture moving seemed inadequate; after a few moments I began to believe that I had been the victim of an hallucination, and then as there was no repetition I thought no more of it.

The following morning I paid one of my very rare visits to the Mamounia Hotel, known to the British public largely through the patronage of Sir Winston Churchill. I went there to meet some English acquaintances who were holidaying in Morocco and who did not share my preference for the *medina*. The conversation was desultory when, after a few minutes, we were joined by a fellow hotel guest of theirs, a well-groomed and monosyllabic colonel whose manner suggested that he found both thought and speech to be irksome.

'Worried about John,' he said at length. 'Went to Agadir – there's been an earthquake there.'

'Surely you must mean Dakar, dear?' said a vague feminine voice. 'Agadir's quite near here, you know.'

'What would John be doing in Dakar?' asked the colonel testily. 'He went to Agadir and there's been an earthquake there. Worried, don't you know.'

'Oh, I expect he's all right,' said the female voice. 'It can't have been much, can it?' The ice tinkled in glasses that held long, soothing drinks; silent servants in extravagant Moorish liveries passed to and fro over rich carpets; outside in the sunny tropical garden exotic birds fluted and trilled as they flitted between fruit-laden trees.

Agadir N Irir (usually abbreviated to Agadir, which means only fortress or escarpment, of which there are many in Morocco) had become in a few years the great tourist resort of Southern Morocco; from an insignificant Moorish fishing village there had shot up, during the later years of the French occupation that ended in 1956, an Atlantic riviera of five-star hotels and international bars that drew a certain type of tourist from all over the world. The speed of this development had brought an enormous increase in Moorish and European population, from some five thousand odd in 1936 to nearly 50,000 in 1953. Although the figure was officially no more than 35,000 by 1960, this was probably a considerable underestimate.

An hour after the colonel's laconic (and wholly justified) preoccupation with the fate of John, the wildest rumours were circulating in the streets of Marrakesh, temporarily silenced only by the first official announcements that seemed, even in their pathetic underestimate, to be those of a major disaster. Eight hundred killed and many wounded; the great luxury Hotel Saada gone down like a card castle, burying its full complement of expensive holidaymakers who would have spoken, I thought to myself, as had my acquaintances at the Mamounia.

The truth came very slowly. The next morning the newspapers reported that it was now feared that the dead might number 1,200 and the wounded 2,000; by the following day the speculative figures had risen to 3,000 and 2,500 respectively. That evening I met a friend, a resident French photographer, who had lived for twenty-five years in Marrakesh and who had spent the day in Agadir. He was exhausted, explosive, and seemingly on the edge of nervous collapse. His hands trembled.

'*Je m'excuse,*' he said, '*mais que voulez-vous?* I am suffering from shock – I who in the war was blown up by a mine and am no stranger to death and the dead. This is worse than war – Agadir is a place of horror, you understand? – horror. The press is mad, mad, I tell you! Three thousand dead? – they mock us! *Selon moi* there cannot be less than eight thousand, and that is a minimum. Whole quarters in which not one soul can have lived – just dust – dust that smells of death, so that you must wear a mask or be sick, or both. The limbs of the dead stick up out of the ground as if they were waving to you. It is a place of horror, I tell you, horror.'

Slowly, day by day, the published figures mounted, until they reached and finally passed his estimate; 10,000 dead and 5,000 wounded. The temperature rose to abnormal heights for the season of the year, reading 104 degrees in the shade at Agadir and 97 degrees at Marrakesh. The rapid putrescence of 10,000 corpses made the work of the rescue teams intolerable; it was Ramadan, and while special dispensation was given to the workers by King Mohammed V in his role of Imam or spiritual leader, many refused to accept it, and carried on their dreadful work without food or water. In Marrakesh the strain of daylight fasting that includes all liquid stretched the nerves of a population many of whom had relations in Agadir, and as the true facts filtered through there were scenes of hysterical grief in every street of the town. Loud-speaking cars toured hour by hour, giving names of known survivors, but the information was slender, because a vast number of Gadiri (people of Agadir) had taken refuge in the plains surrounding the town and were camping under the *argan* trees with what possessions they had been able to salvage in their flight. The government put out an appeal for all refugees to report their names to the nearest authority, cheikh, caid, pasha, or governor; but among this new race of nomads there would be many whom the message would not reach for weeks or even months. Sometimes, too, the loudspeakers would announce that no further survivors might be expected from this or that quarter of the town; the car would pass on leaving scattered figures prostrate and weeping in the dust.

Tales of strange portents preceding the earthquake came from many sources. A few minutes before the first tremors all the dogs of the town had begun to howl in unison, cats wailed and prowled, mules and donkeys struggled with their tethers. An English couple at the cinema had a premonition of some cataclysm and left the building for the beach, where, as the first tremors shook the ground beneath them, they saw a column of fire shoot up out of the sea. A man returning from a café saw a

6

great flight of ravens alight for a moment upon the houses and then take off in commotion and calling.

The survivors remembered the noise more than the movement of the ground; the roar of toppling buildings and the screams of human beings who fell with them. All lighting was extinguished with the first quake, and those who were able to struggle free and to search among rubble and ruin for their children worked in the confusion of total darkness and the noise of all hell. The first rescuers on the scene, the French Marines, brought only pinpoints of light, so that for long sound predominated over sight.

It is a point of enormous significance that the vast majority of those who survived the first two seismic tremors believed unquestioningly that the disaster must be universal; it was not to them the end of Agadir but the end of the world, or even of the universe. The darkness and the din, the pain, the pressure of the fallen stone were illimitable; outside that world there could not exist elsewhere any other that they had known before. Thus the historians of biblical times recorded that strictly local flooding of the Tigris-Euphrates basin as the Great Flood, world-wide because it went beyond the limit of their physical vision; and wove round Noah a myth as the saviour of every animal species, unknowing that the continuation of all life, animal and human, went on unhindered and unhelped, helpless and hopeful, outside the puddle of his flood.

There is lapidary evidence for the historical truth of what in biblical civilisation came to be known as The Flood; even its date can be estimated with some accuracy at 3000 B.C. Between the Hebrew and the Sumerian versions of this story there are only minor divergencies, and if it is a surprise to realise that there was more than one ark afloat, it must be remembered that greater or lesser floods were certainly common in Mesopotamia, and some technique for saving the lives and livestock of a family or tribe had probably been standardised, as had also the technique of releasing birds to search for land. 'The' Flood was, plainly, the greatest that had been known, and thus its chroniclers crammed the whole world into the narrow confines of the lowlands lying to the north-west of the Persian Gulf.

Seton Lloyd in his *Twin Rivers* describes the discovery, in the mid-nineteenth century, of 25,073 inscribed clay tablets in the palaces of King Sennacherib and King Ashur-bani-pal at Nineveh, the better part of two royal libraries, which when deciphered some fifteen years later at the British Museum, yielded the Chaldean account of the flood.

The account of the flood which emerged from all this was every bit as dramatic as the Biblical version. It concerned a patriach called Utu-nipishtim, whose home was at Shuruppak on the Euphrates. Like Noah, he was approached by the god Ea, who told him of the impending doom of the earth and commanded him to build a boat, giving some details about its size and construction. This done, he complied with Ea's further wish that he should load it with 'all that he possessed and all the seed of life'. Utu-nipishtim continues the story: 'I made to go up into the ship and my family and kinsfolk, the cattle of the field, the beasts of the field, all handicraftsmen, I made them go up into it.' As the appointed time of the deluge drew near, he watched the aspect of the approaching storm. 'Terror possessed me to look upon it. I went into the ship and shut my door. . . . The water attacked the people like a battle. Brother saw not brother. Men could not be recognised from heaven. Even the gods were terrified at the cyclone. They shrank back and went up into the heaven of Anu. The gods crouched like a dog and cowered by the wall. . . .' For six days the wind and the storm raged and the cyclone overwhelmed the land. 'When the seventh day came the cyclone ceased, the storm and the battle which had fought like an army.' At the same time the ship 'grounded on the mountain of Nizir' and after 'opening the air hole' Utu-nipishtim began the same sort of investigation as Noah made, 'brought out a dove and let her go free, but because she had no place to alight on she came back. I brought out a swallow and let her go free, but because she had no place to alight on she came back. I brought out a raven and let her go free; the raven flew away, she saw the sinking water. She ate. She waded and splashed but came not back.' Again like

8

Noah he now emerged from his ship and sacrificed to the gods and 'the gods gathered together like flies over him that sacrificed'.

These situations in which local cataclysm is assumed to be universal would seem to be at the opposite pole to animistic beliefs in which every disaster is assumed to be aimed specifically at the individual or the tribe; but there is in fact a meeting-point in the conception that 'we have *all* offended the gods'.

It was only when daylight came, and the survivors could see, not only that beyond Agadir the face of land and sea looked as before, but also that there were undamaged buildings and living human beings in the town itself, that the truth became plain to them.

The extent of the damage in different quarters varied not only with the type of building construction, but also with the altitude above sea-level, so that the houses built upon the rock cliff on the northern side stood better than those at a lower level; in many cases, as in that of the Mauretania Hotel, from which many Austrian, Dutch and Danish holidaymakers escaped alive, their façades crashed but left the main internal structure intact. The Hotel Saada, in contrast, built almost upon the beach, collapsed totally, but in slow motion, the roof sliding out from the walls until the unbalance crumbled them too. From the Saada, one of the great luxury hotels of the town, there were very few survivors from the eighty-odd tourist residents who had dined in the hotel. One of these was Robin Maugham, whom I had met in Rabat a few weeks before. He had come to Morocco in search of a story, not background material for a novel but something sensational that would stand being written up by itself. When I had met him he had been in the country for some weeks and found nothing to his taste; as a newspaper had given him a considerable sum of money for his journey he felt that his position was becoming embarrassing. I was fortunately able to redeem him from his predicament by giving him the outline and references of a story that was the apotheosis of all that he could wish, the then inadequately and ill-reported story of the Hillal Oil. The manufacturers of this poor quality olive-oil had adulterated their product with engine-oil bought from American bases, thereby causing in one day the paralysis of thousands of people in the city of Meknes. The dogged attempts of one doctor to diagnose the new disease; his search, at first in vain, for any common dietetic factor among his patients; his sudden realisation that the material in which the varying foods had been cooked might be the key; his flying of a sample to Europe for analysis; the call-out of the army to round up every bottle of Hillal Oil in the country, and the doctor's triumphant arrest of the whole epidemic in an almost unbelievably short space of time – all these made high drama, and Robin Maugham was well satisfied. I had met him again in Marrakesh a few days before the earthquake; he had finished his research and now felt justified in taking a few days' holiday at the Saada Hotel in Agadir. On the morning after the earthquake, I said to a mutual acquaintance, 'I'm afraid Robin Maugham must have been killed; there's something oddly pathetic about his dying in an episode he would so much have wanted to report.' My companion hesitated, and then said almost diffidently, as if he were indulging too extravagant a flight of fantasy, 'Doesn't he somehow strike you as being someone who will always fall on his feet? He was looking for a "story" in Morocco – do you know I could almost believe that he was in that hotel and somehow survived and got a unique story?' The next morning I read among the slender list of survivors 'Rollin viscomte Morgan, diplomate Anglais'. He had been imprisoned under a fallen beam, with just enough room for his body and no more, for many hours; eventually he was extricated, by great skill and luck, unharmed but noticeably garrulous, and packed off to England to write his scoop.

Opposite to the Saada the Prefecture, built according to seismic-resisting principles, stood completely intact. All houses built of *pisé* (mud walls packed wet between shaping-boards and then allowed to bake dry in the sun) were demolished, not so much into rubble as into dust, so that the bodies of the dead and their erstwhile household possessions were the only solid things remaining. The old Kasbah, built on the summit overlooking the town fell as a tree falls, and out of its 800 inhabitants only fifty survived. The main *medina*, Talbourdjt, built of *pisé* in the typical Moorish way, collapsed with all its *souq*, mosques, schools, and warrens of small dwellings; from its 5,000 inhabitants the survivors were counted on the fingers of two hands. Too long a task, surely, for Mr Thornton Wilder. Because of this total destruction, rescue work in Talbourdjt was impossible. Here were no fallen blocks of masonry under or between which unseen survivors might have been trapped as Robin Maugham had been; there could be nothing but the dead. So these areas were ignored until the great heat and the terrible stench made impossible even the recovery of bodies. The rescue workers concentrated upon the areas of heavy fallen masonry where life might still, however improbably, linger. By Saturday March 5th, when I left Marrakesh to spend two nights in Rabat before returning to London on Monday, the information was more exact. Apart from the great mass of Moroccan dead, 850 of the Spanish community of 2,000 had been killed and as many wounded; the old fishing village of Founti had been utterly razed; there had been almost total casualties among the women workers of the great sardine canneries; 100 Italians were missing, 37 British. Of Moroccan official bodies the heaviest casualties had been among the 8th Battalion of the Royal Armed Forces in barracks, and among the *gendarmerie* or country police. The headquarters of the police proper had not been damaged significantly, but because it was the season of Ramadan its members had leave of absence during the night, and they died in the cafés, cinemas, private houses or unofficial brothels where they were relaxing from their second day of fast.

The occurrence of the disaster during the season of Ramadan had still further repercussions among the survivors. Although the rule that nothing may pass the lips between sunrise and sunset does not, according to orthodoxy, apply to the sick or those who are journeying, there were many who believed that the fast would have been broken if they received medicine, and a considerable number of the wounded even refused blood transfusion on that score.

The Crown Prince Moulay Hassan, now King Hassan II, had taken charge at his father's orders, and from a temporary head-quarters at Inezgane, a few kilometres from the ruined city, he acted with speed and decision, decision that to those who did not fully understand the situation he was facing seemed callous and brutal.

By sunrise on Friday conditions in what was left of Agadir were so terrible as to demand ruthless measures against the grow-ing probability of epidemic. Prince Hassan had no reasonable choice. The temperature at mid-morning had reached 105 degrees, and the smell of putrescence extended to a radius of three miles outside the town. The workers in the ruins now wore gas-masks or breathing pads, and their hands were gloved. Those areas where rescue was considered impossible were treated with quick-lime to destroy the bodies; if it destroyed living bodies as well as the dead there was no alternative. Rats, driven upwards by the blocking and drying of the sewers in which they lived, were everywhere among the rubble and ruins; dogs and innumerable stray cats fed upon every exposed corpse; over all hung a hum-ming pall of flies. Even in this place of horror furtive looters skulked among the ruins and took rings and bracelets from the dead; some of these, when challenged, claimed that they had lingered on in the town searching in despair for a lost child.

By order of Moulay Hassan the last inhabitants were removed from the city and its confines were sealed by military barricades. Looters were shot at sight and their bodies thrown among those endless ranks awaiting a common grave. All livestock loose among the ruins were killed. Great quantities of rat poison were laid throughout the whole ruined city; D.D.T. and disinfectants were sprayed constantly from lorries and hovering helicopters. Fifty bulldozers continued inch by inch to work wherever there remained a remote chance of life.

On arrival at Rabat on Saturday evening I met, in the house of a mutual friend, Moulay Ahmed El Alaoui, a cousin of the king and then Chief of Press Services at the Royal Palace. The king, he told me, was paying his third visit to Agadir the next morning, this time in company with all the diplomatic representatives and press attachés; there were two aircraft leaving Rabat at eight a.m., and he would secure me a seat in one of these if I wished. He arrived in a palace car at seven-twenty the next morning to carry my host and myself to the airport.

Moulay Ahmed, of whom I shall have more to say in a later chapter, is one of the many phenomena of the new independent Morocco. He is a dynamo working at such incredible pressure that one feels he must blow up; he is everywhere at once, doing a hundred jobs at once, with the same sort of furious impatience. He was very close to the king and had his ear, so that his work always extended far beyond its official designation. Because of his tireless energy and apparent ability to work without sleep (he may arrive for a chat at a friend's house, unannounced, at any hour between midnight and six a.m., and he was popularly believed to sleep from six a.m. until seven a.m., though there is no positive evidence of this), because of this energy it devolved upon him, for example, to plan the innumerable details of King Mohammed V's 1960 tour of the whole Middle East and the Holy Cities, and to supervise the entire daily routine of the un-wieldy touring court. With this background knowledge of his exalted position it was at first a shock to me to realise that it was he himself who carried out much of the petty administration of his own decisions, with a complete and characteristic disregard of formalities. One of the happier anecdotes, of which a volume might be collected, as could also a volume of the less fortunate, concerns his office as Minister of Tourism. Motoring between Rabat and Casablanca, he encountered a party of Swedish tourists whose car towed a caravan, and who were proceeding in the opposite direction, that is, towards Rabat. He immediately ordered his chauffeur to turn the car and to pursue and overtake the Swedes. This accomplished, he dismounted and stopped the tourists as a traffic policeman would. He then asked them if they were going to Rabat and if they had anywhere to camp. Moulay Ahmed is not always of ministerial appearance, and it was with some astonishment and apprehension that the visitors replied that they had not yet made any definite arrangements. 'Then,' said Moulay Ahmed, with all the great charm of which he is capable, 'let me introduce myself. I am the Minister of Tourism, and you shall camp in the forecourt of the Ministry itself. I myself shall accompany you there now.' Abandoning whatever project he had been engaged upon he led his prisoners back triumphantly to the capital; for several days thereafter the amazed population of Rabat could observe a party of foreigners camping in the gracious and conspicuously placed forecourt of the Ministry, drying laundry fluttering merrily from a line attached to the caravan. Swedes are notoriously unselfconscious people.

It was only to be expected, therefore, that it was Moulay Ahmed himself who at the airport controlled, manually when necessary, the variegated hordes of press attachés and journalists, shouting out the list of names, pushing back those who were in the wrong stream, pulling forward bodily those who were vague or misunderstanding, alternately a brusque bus conductor and a statesman, an irritable usher and a high administrator. After half an hour or more of this separation of sheep from goats the two aircraft took off for Agadir, the one containing the king, his ministers and the foreign ambassadors, and the other the press attachés and members of the international press.

From Agadir Airport the party left as a long convoy of vehicles; first the military motor-cycle and security police out-riders, then the royal cars boxed-in by further motor-cycles, then a busload of ambassadors and another of the press. The cinematographers had been grouped by Moulay Ahmed's unique combination of force and cajolery into a sort of loose pyramid upon a jeep; near the summit of this pyramid he chose, capriciously, to perch himself. On the roof of the press bus travelled a few hardy photographers who had decided to brave the various odours of which they had been warned.

The procession drove straight to the town, across the flat lands of *argan* trees, round whose trunks and spiny branches were visible everywhere the improvised homes of the destitute – blankets hung or stretched as screens between limb and trunk, a handful of salvaged possessions by a camp-fire at their sides. Men, women and children lined the roadside to see the passage of the king, for, though this was his third visit since the earthquake, his presence was of far greater significance than would be that of a British monarch in parallel circumstances, for since the Sultan of Morocco is the spiritual leader of his people, in him reposes the power of *baraka*, or blessing.

At the road-barrier guarding the dead town's entrance macabrely masked figures sprayed each vehicle in turn with white clouds of disinfectant. The procession with its outriders began very slowly to tour the streets of what had been Agadir.

The image was not, in effect, greatly different from that presented by any town destroyed by aerial bombardment; here were the same crazily leaning walls, the same mass of broken glass; the same tumbled heaps of masonry and scattered household goods; the same walls torn off to reveal the cascading chaos of furnished rooms; the same houses that stood, arbitrarily, while their neighbours had fallen. Only in one respect did it differ significantly – the great areas that were no more than fine dust, now whitened with quicklime, through which but few solid objects protruded. Some of these objects were extremely unpleasant. Where the rubble was more solid, more capable of containing life – however improbably after six days of blazing heat – masked rescue workers were still moving masonry; elsewhere bulldozers moved among the debris with the infinite slowness of a dream.

The occupants of the bus clamoured that every window should be kept closed; opening mine a little, I found that the air reeked of disinfectant and D.D.T., with a sour-sickly undertone that made it possible to imagine the unspeakable conditions of the previous day. Behind me I heard an English voice say: 'I don't see any rats and I can't smell much except hospital smells; I think this story's been overwritten.' I wanted to ask him whether the story of one death can be overwritten; this should have been a funeral cortège for 10,000 dead among whose bodies we were even now passing, and the brisk on-the-job attitude of the horde of journalists to whom this was – it appeared – no more than a news item to be covered, seemed harshly jarring.

As the procession drew abreast of the remains of the Hôtel-de-Ville, each car became enveloped in a grey cloud of D.D.T. through which were dimly visible masked riflemen standing grotesquely at the present for the passage of the royal cars; they moved on down the Boulevard Mohammed V, officially opened by the king amid the cheering ranks of Agadir's citizens only a few months before. There was no halt on this weird tour of a city so newly dead; again the cars reached the road block, were sprayed by dim, masked figures, and moved out into the world of the living. For me the nearest parallel in my experience was emerging from the suffocation of drowning, which not only entails a struggle, as did for me this equivalent proximity to mass death, but contains also a contact with negation, a sharp and shrivelling awareness of the enemy at hand and allies unprepared.

From Agadir the cumbersome cortège took the road for Inezgane and royal inspection of the emergency camps for the destitute. The first of these had been completed less than twenty-four hours before; an accommodation settlement of British Army tents ranged on flat open ground, with a minor clinic at which the injured who came in from their shelters in the surrounding country could, according to the gravity of their condition, be treated or sent on to the new medical camp. Already this settlement held 1,300 of the homeless, and four more similar camps were projected to house the remainder as they could be located and brought in. Some 15,000 people had left the ruins; many were camping in the surrounding countryside, as yet unaware of any arrangements made for them; still others were known to have reached far-off towns and villages.

In this first camp were many children, and these, seemingly unperturbed by terrors now five days old, were playing organised games and doing P.T. exercises under the leadership of Muslim Boy Scouts. Many others, however, were showing symptoms of delayed shock, and were waiting transfer to one of the hospital camps. The orderly rows of tents, the green turf, the strolling ambassadors (some of whom were taking photographs of each other against suitable backgrounds), the royal presence and the extravagant greeting accorded to him, all combined to impart to this camp an air almost of fête.

The next halting-point of the royal procession was the first of the hospital camps. Here were newly arrived units of British, German, Swiss and Italian Red Cross, with well-equipped surgeries and X-ray plants; but as yet there were very few patients, for many had still to be transferred from the naval base to which they had first been taken, and more than 2,000 had already been flown to the hospitals of the great cities of Morocco. The German unit, for example, had six patients, one of whom had only been dug out the evening before, and had thus survived four days of deep interment.

There was no time to linger here, for in contrast to the leisurely atmosphere at the first settlement, the party now swept along at the heels of the king as he dived into tent after tent before hurrying back to his car, and it required the omnipresence of Moulay Ahmed to ensure that something rather more than a handful of ambassadors and pressmen did not swell the numbers of the displaced at each successive camp visited. Many of the party began to flag in the heat and the dust, but the king seemed tireless, a dignified figure in a grey *djellabah* and white *babuch* that kicked aside the spiny litter of fallen *argan* twigs as though they were as well used to the harsh ground of the *bled* as to red carpets and the marble mosaic of palace floors. On the day of his first visit many had remarked upon the deep despair of his appearance as he walked among the ruins with an oft-repeated gesture of upraised palms; now his expression seemed one of determination, the jaw set and his hands often momentarily clenched.

In the early afternoon, while he rested for a few moments at the Crown Prince's headquarters at Inezgane, fresh tremors shook the ground, no stronger than those I had felt at Marrakesh, but enough to make me wonder whether all this work might not be wasted. Some two hours later, as the two aircraft took off for Rabat and passed over the bay, a strange turmoil of water moved the sea between the shore and the squadron of French warships lying at anchor, as though some great mass were being pushed up from below. It was difficult to judge how this must have appeared from sea-level, but it was alarming enough for the squadron to weigh anchor hurriedly and stand a mile farther out to sea.

There was no general scientific agreement as to the cause of the earthquake; one thing seemed certain, that many years would pass before Agadir again became a recreation ground that tourists would trust. Despite this, the king's gesture of faith was to announce that rebuilding was to begin immediately, and that the new city would be officially inaugurated in a year's time, on March 2nd 1961 – the anniversary of Independence Day, whose celebrations were changed so terribly to tears in 1960.

Tragic majesty, Sidi Mohammed Ben Youssef, Mohammed V, King and Sultan of Morocco, eleventh and most enlightened ruler of the long Alaouite dynasty – kidnapped and banished when he aspired for the future of his country against the exploitation of French 'protection'; exiled first to cold Corsica (where he was made to pay even the wages of the numerous police who guarded him); from there transferred, as a potential threat to Mediterranean peace, to pass two years in a ruinous and roof-leaking hotel in Madagascar; tragic majesty, who would never lead the celebrations of another Independence Day. On February 26th 1961, Agadir little changed, Mohammed V was absolved from all earthly necessity for explanation, and Morocco was in mourning for her first national hero. No one has ever announced the inauguration of a new Agadir.

2

Return to Camusfeàrna

I HAD learned, the day before I visited Agadir, of a minor tragedy in my Chelsea house, but the human holocaust in Morocco had deadened the bitter little sting of pain that I feel upon the death of creatures for which I have made myself responsible.

The houses of the Square where I live when in London are of small rooms, in four floors. (They were, I believe, artisans' houses until after the First World War, and upon learning from my late charlady that she remembered the house when its tenant was a police constable, I asked her how he had occupied all the space. 'Well,' she said, 'they used to have a lodger, and then of course there were the servants.' My eyebrows must have shot up. 'Oh yes, they always had a married couple to look after them – never a hand's turn would the missus do, but ring the bell in the sitting-room for tea or whatever it was that she or his nibs wanted.') After Chelsea squares became fashionable the ground-floor back and front of these houses were, in most cases, knocked into one, giving a single long room of some twenty-five feet, with the structural supports of the old division projecting some eighteen inches from each wall. In the garden end of this room I was wont to work when I was in London, and in the other I had accumulated, slowly and almost by chance it seemed, a small collection of brilliant tropical birds, who flew at liberty and fed upon fruit suspended from natural branches. This collection had begun with an unwanted gift of two gem-like mites that I had for a time kept in a large and elaborate Victorian birdcage;

19

eventually, having a dislike for the concept of caged birds, I liberated them in the room, and was so struck by their beauty in flight that I added another pair of a different species. The first had been tanagers, a South American group which contains some of the most brilliantly coloured birds in the world, and soon the addition of new tanager species became a minor, dilettante hobby. Certainly it was one mainly of sensory titillation, for we arranged concealed spotlamps to light the jewels in their wings as they flew, and papered the walls above the bookcases black so that none of the iridescence of the feathers should be lost by silhouette. By the spring of 1960 there were some fourteen of these birds, including one species that had rarely been kept successfully before. Most of them would fly down and take food from the hand.

The necessary temperature in this room was maintained by an oil stove, and one night a week or so before my return to London from Morocco, some irregularity of wick or paraffin feed had started a fire. The circumstances that caused this never became clear, but it was a slow, smouldering fire giving off a dense smoke and covering walls and ceiling with an oily black soot. Jimmy Watt, who had spent the winter in London with Edal the otter (for Camusfeàrna was not yet a place of permanent residence), had not been awoken by the fumes until too late, and all the birds were dead.

Edal, however, was unharmed. She occupied a basement room of her own, with a tunnel through the wall into the garden, and she slept peacefully even through the pandemonium of the fire brigade's arrival; considering, perhaps, that the unseemly din above her was some typically tiresome human prank of no concern to her. So I returned, weighed down by the image of Agadir as few other secondhand experiences had affected me before; sad, but mocking myself for being so, at the death of my birds whose wings seemed to have borne along so many sentences that without their inspiration would have been lumberingly pedestrian; as yet unquestioning that I should find Edal ready to return to Camusfeàrna and renew the idyll, unquestioning that the refuge, the pool of silence, could go on and on for ever.

When we had been separated in the past she had been used to

greet me as does a dog after its master's prolonged absence, and when I walked into her room now I expected a demonstrative welcome. She was curled up on the bed, and when I called her name she barely lifted her head. She looked at me vaguely and immediately curled up again. At first I thought she was sleepy and had not recognised me; only slowly did I begin to understand that she was very ill. She had eaten nothing, I was told, for two full days.

It was the beginning of a three weeks' struggle, the first of two in six months, to save her life. Immediate veterinary tests showed the presence of liver fluke; it was not generally suspected then, as it is now, that this parasite with its curious multi-stage life cycle is probably endemic in otters and causes no damage to function unless present in vast numbers, and Edal was therefore treated for liver fluke as being the root cause of her symptoms. Under this treatment, which made her constantly sick, her condition deteriorated rapidly, and she became extremely emaciated. When further tests showed the presence of Shigella dysentry, we decided to abandon interest in the flukes altogether.

Her treatment was not easy. In her own room she would not allow the vet to examine her or to inject her, and he suggested that from the psychological viewpoint her submission would be much more probable in the alien atmosphere of his surgery. In this he proved right, as he did also in suggesting a method of restraint that appeared to me wholly impracticable. It was necessary to give her three separate injections in quick succession every day, besides taking her temperature rectally, and granted that no wild animal could be expected to undergo these painful indignities without protest, we had somehow to restrain her head from turning. Edal wore a harness, not a collar, because an otter's head is so little wider than the neck that a collar can always be slipped; now the vet suggested that if she wore two collars, with the lead attached to the hindmost one, the bunching up of the skin would keep them in position. This idea proved entirely successful, and every day Edal was immobilised on the operating table by three separate leads strained in different directions. It was strange that, as the drive to the surgery and the repetition of this ordeal became a daily routine, she showed no antipathy either to the waiting-room or the surgery; she never shied away from its door and she would sit on one of our laps, among the dogs, cats, parrots and other household pets that form the bulk of a city vet's practice. When the time came for her to be carried down to the surgery and laid upon the operating table she made no protest.

For a fortnight or so there was little change. At best she had an even chance of living, and though we tempted her with every kind of dainty she would eat nothing of her own free will; we had all this time to feed her forcibly with concentrated liquids.

At last one morning I noticed, as we drove down the King's Road on our daily visit to the surgery, that she seemed for the first time to be taking a little of her old interest in the traffic and the passers-by; she even hauled herself up to put her paws against the glass and peer, a little myopically, out of the passengers' window. In the waiting-room she was restless, and in the surgery she eyed the vet with distinct disfavour. He looked at her and said: 'I do believe we've done the trick. This morning she looks for the first time like a truly viable animal.' The same afternoon I opened her door quietly and looked round it, half expecting to find her inert upon the bed as she had been for so long, but she was engaged in guzzling a plate of scrambled eggs, stuffing her mouth full with those curious little simian hands just as she used to do. It was the first solid food, indeed the only food that she had eaten voluntarily, for sixteen days.

From then on she made a steady recovery; by April 14th she was her usual high-spirited and inquisitive self, and greeted a TV unit with all her old enthusiasm for novelties. She was, moreover, extremely patient with the constant retakes requisite to the threadbare story scripted for her by the BBC. (Mr Macdonald Hastings, the viewing public were asked to believe, had been astonished to see in the King's Road an otter at the heels of Jimmy Watt and myself. Fortunately, having a whole television unit with him, he and it followed us home unobserved and noted the number on our door. By what disembodiment he was then assumed to have passed through that door it is difficult to imagine, for the next scene showed him peering, unannounced, round the door of my sitting-room and registering delighted surprise at the sight of Edal sitting on my lap.)

A few days later she travelled up to Camusfeàrna by train with Jimmy. As in the past with other otters, I contrived that she should share his first-class sleeper, but as before she required a dog ticket. This time, instead of leaving blank the space for description of the dog, I indulged a flight of fantasy, and wrote 'Illyrian Poodle'. This breed is not of my invention but of Mr William Burroughs, and figures briefly in *The Naked Lunch*.

Manhattan Serenade: A. J. and entourage start into New York night-club. A.J. is leading a purple-assed baboon on a gold chain. A.J. is dressed in checked linen plus-fours with a cashmere jacket.
Manager: *Wait* a minute. Wait a *minute*. What's that?
A.J.: It's an Illyrian poodle. Chicest beast a man can latch onto. It'll raise the tone of your trap.
Manager: I suspect it to be a purple-assed baboon and it stands outside.
Stooge: Don't you know who this is? It's A.J., last of the big-time spenders.
Manager: Leave him take his purple-assed bastard and big time spend some place else.
. . . A.J. drives a gold stake into the floor and pickets the baboon.

I cannot leave A.J. without even introducing him. He is:

actually of obscure Near East extraction – had at one time come on like an English gentleman. His English accent waned with the British Empire, and after World War II he became an American by Act of Congress. . . . It is rumoured that he represents a trust of giant insects from another galaxy . . . A.J.'s cover story? An international playboy and harmless practical joker. It was A.J. who put the pirhana fish in Lady Sutton-Smith's swimming-pool, and dosed the punch with a

23

mixture of Yage, Hashish and Yohimbine during a Fourth of July reception at the U.S. Embassy, precipitating an orgy. Ten prominent citizens – American, of course – subsequently died of shame.

The ticket-puncher looked at Edal without great curiosity. 'What's that?' he asked. 'Illyrian poodle.' 'Huh? Never saw one of them before. Sort of a dog, is it?' 'Sort of,' I said. The joke had fallen a little flat.

Before Edal and Jimmy had left for Scotland there had taken place a further one of those coincidences that make my experiences with otters read like fiction rather than fact. To appreciate the extent of the coincidence it should be understood that the West African species of otter to which Edal belongs has very rarely been brought to this country at all, and never, so far as I know, had there been a specimen bottle-reared from blind help-lessness as Edal had been by Dr Malcolm Macdonald. Now a Mr and Mrs Davin, on short leave from Sierra Leone, telephoned to me to say that they had brought to England with them a male otter cub that they had acquired unweaned in Africa and had reared on a bottle. The cub had already been promised to a country gentleman whom they had met on the boat, but they would like me at least to see it.

Presently their car was at the door. I did not want to bring the cub into the house, for fear that some trace of Edal's infection might linger there; this was doubly important, as his owners explained to me, for not only did he eat with his fingers as did Edal, but he also had a baby habit of sucking them, especially when confronted with unfamiliar surroundings. Mr Davin reached into a travelling-box in the back of the car, and emerged with a superb ball of dark chocolate-coloured, almost black, plush; this in his arms uncoiled and re-formed as a small, stout otter lying on its back. It put three fingers of its right hand into its mouth and began to suck noisily, looking about it with interest.

This otter seemed more completely domesticated than even

24

Edal had been. It was the hour when the local school empties, and the children began to crowd round, screaming and laughing and calling to their distant companions, the bolder ones trying to touch him. To most animals, and more particularly to most wild animals, a surrounding crowd of vocal children and advancing hands would constitute a situation of fear, but this otter seemed in no way disconcerted; indeed it was clear that he considered them as potential playmates from whom he was being unjustly withheld. I coveted this creature; already in my mind's eye I could see him and Edal gambolling together under the waterfall at Camusfeàrna or porpoising after each other in the calm blue waters of the bay below the house; already I was mentally enlarging the size of the otter bed in the cottage kitchen.

Teko (he had been named after an up-country veterinary station in Sierra Leone, without his owners being aware that 'Tek' is in fact an Old English word for otter) was not content in the Surrey home to which, after our meeting, he had been taken, and when I learned that Mr and Mrs Davin intended anyway to visit the West Highlands during their holiday, bringing Teko with them, I felt that the warmth of his welcome would be so great both from humans and from Edal as to leave his owners no room for choice about his future. As in the case of Dr Malcolm Macdonald, they would have somehow to find a home for him before returning to West Africa, and I knew that few households were allowed to revolve round the life of otters as mine did at that date. I reckoned, however, without Edal's highly developed sense of property.

I arrived at Camusfeàrna a few days after Jimmy and Edal; I watched her revel anew in the freedom of stream and sea after her long winter sojourn in the drab confines of her London quarters, and in the fair golden weather that in those days seemed never to desert Camusfeàrna for long – it seemed to be the beginning of just such another summer idyll as the last. But there was to be no idyll, then or thereafter, for I had left the calm reaches of the river.

I had been at Camusfeàrna a fortnight or so when Mr and Mrs Davin arrived in the neighbourhood and found themselves lodgings some twelve miles away. By now they had more or less made up their minds that if Camusfeàrna seemed a suitable home for Teko they would leave him with me. I had provided them with a harness for him, so that his introduction to Edal could be carried out with the greatest caution and both animals under restraint. This policy paid dividends, for without our forethought there would have been little left of the unfortunate Teko. A year before, when Edal first arrived, any other animal was a welcome playmate; then, I am sure, she would have taken Teko to her heart with delight, but by now I entertained a suspicion that jealousy and possessiveness played no small part in her make-up, and I was determined that this first meeting should leave nothing to chance.

On the green sward of the field in which Camusfeàrna stands Mr and Mrs Davin waited with Teko on a lead, while I went upstairs, clipped Edal's lead to her harness and led her out. At first she did not see him, for the group stood among scattered clumps of rushes, but she saw strangers, and stood on her hind legs like a penguin to get a better view, for otters are myopic, and of their five senses trust their eyesight perhaps the least. (So, incidentally, do human beings, or at least place it secondarily to the sense of touch; the idea of a ghost or any other supernatural phenomenon having its root in the principle of intangibility, touch remaining our one final test of 'reality'. For an otter, a ghost would, I presume, consist of some being that could not be smelled, and something that had no smell could not be 'real'.) Then she advanced a few paces and stood up again. She was then no more than ten or fifteen yards from the group, and this time she saw Teko. Her nostrils wiggled frantically, and at last she caught a whiff of his scent. She uttered a shriek of anger, and made a dash for him that almost pulled me off my feet. It was not an encouraging start. For a quarter of an hour we walked the two otters along the beach and about the field, always at a respectful distance from each other, while Edal kept up a running commentary of rage in that high, screaming wail which of all the animal cries I have heard sounds the most vindictive. Then I took her back to her room in the house, and Teko's owners and I conferred, as do generals when they have reluctantly to agree that they are attacking an unassailable position.

It seemed to us that the place of their meeting might affect her attitude, for otters are territorial animals, and that she might be more willing to accept him if the encounter were to take place on neutral ground over which Edal did not feel herself to reign supreme. The following day we made a second attempt, on the road above Camusfeàrna, but there was no noticeable improvement. Then we took Edal to the vicinity of the house where Mr and Mrs Davin were lodging twelve miles away. Here it seemed to me that she had begun to tolerate his presence a little, and her hymn of hate was not quite so continuous. There were, to use a printer's metaphor, more white spaces in the previously unbroken text of vituperation. She was, consciously, I think, lulling us into a sense of false security, hoping all the while for an opportunity which when it came left no doubt of her intentions. We were at the moment in single file, and she was walking beside me quite silently a few paces behind Teko and his owners, when he lagged a little behind them and gave her the chance for which she had been waiting so patiently. With a bound and a scream she had him by the tail and was worrying it like a dog trying to kill a rat. I contrived to haul her off almost in the same instant as it happened, and Teko fled whimpering pathetically to the consoling hands of his foster parents, while Edal's voice rose to a positive paean of hate and triumph.

The following day I watched Teko's departure with profound disappointment; Edal's intransigent attitude to the question of consorts had posed a problem to which I could see no solution. Time was short and Teko's owners were wasting their leave in searching for a home for him; while they did so I offered them the use of my London house with its otter room and tunnel to the garden.

Suitable homes for otters are not, however, easy to find, and it was no very great surprise to me when, little more than a fortnight later, they approached me again to ask how long it would take us to prepare separate quarters for Teko, who, they pointed out, had never been accustomed to freedom, and was conspicuously easy to entertain. I did not yet fully believe in Edal's permanent hostility towards him. Teko seemed to me an infinitely desirable creature, and I disliked the thought of his being placed in hands less tender and experienced than my own. I replied that it would take between a fortnight and three weeks.

In the event, however, no more than a week was available, and though fortunately most of the necessary materials were to hand, Jimmy and I had to work far into every night and begin again at dawn. I had foreseen that after the publication of *Ring of Bright Water* more and more uninvited visitors would find their way to the house, and visualising that these might be accompanied by dogs unfriendly to otters I had decided to enclose a small piece of land surrounding the house with a continuous five-foot-high wooden paling. The wood for this formidable undertaking had been delivered by sea (the twine tying the planks into bundles of forty had in many cases broken as the cargo was lowered overboard and the whole bay had been bobbing with timber as difficult to round up as had been my Shetland sheep on Soay years before), and now lay above the tide-line on the beach below the house. With this wood we decided to construct for Teko a separate enclosure at one end of the cottage, where was also a small lean-to outhouse that might be converted to his use. Even in the early days storage space at Camusfeàrna had always been a problem, and over the years the contents of this modest building had become an inextricable jumble of lobster pots, ropes, paint tins, tools, boxes of nails and every imaginable form of junk, so that to extract any desired object from it had long since become a major task, necessitating both time and patience. Below this entangled miscellany the floor was covered several inches deep in coal-dust and debris.

Teko was an animal accustomed to living in human houses, and to lodge him in accommodation that did not in some sense resemble a human room would have been as inappropriate as to chain a drawing-room Pekinese to a barrel of straw in the open. In that week, then, we were required to reclaim, repaint and furnish the outhouse; to enclose a piece of land with wooden paling; to sink wire-netting deep into the ground against the possibility of Teko digging his way out; to construct some form of lavatory for him that would be easy to keep clean (the Specialist would have been hard pressed to do better), to dig and cement a pool in which he could play, and to lead running-water to it. With these basic conditions as his background, Teko could then be entertained in the living-room at any time when Edal was confined to her own quarters, and he could accompany us for walks or swims behind the dinghies after she had been exercised. The keeping of these two otters did, it is true, appear likely to become a full-time job; but as a visitor remarked, not without malice, this was perhaps as good a way of earning an anti-social living as any other.

All this work we completed in the week at our disposal, and though the cement was still damp enough to take the imprint of Teko's feet as he entered, and the paint was barely dry upon the walls of his house, he appeared entranced with his new quarters; never once did he whimper or call or behave otherwise than as if the place had always been his home. I put a camp-bed in his house and for the first few nights I slept there myself, for sharing sleeping quarters with an animal is the most certain way of establishing mutual confidence. It was not, in this case, an entirely comfortable procedure, for no sooner had I manoeuvred myself into the sleeping-bag than he would begin to explore my face with his simian fingers, pushing mobile digits between my lips and into my nostrils and ears, uttering the while a curious snuffle that led me to believe he had contracted a cold; only after the first few days did I discover that this was a sound of pleasure and contentment, like the purring of a cat. After some half-hour of this demonstrative affection he would squirm down into the warmth of the sleeping-bag and slumber peacefully through the night. Or so I had thought, but on the third morning I awoke to find myself engulfed in a smother of liberated kapok, blocking my nose, eyes and ears; Teko had spent the greater part of the night happily chewing holes in the lining of the sleeping-bag. I have contended, and continue to do so, that otters have a keen sense of humour, almost in the way that these words are used of human beings; the action equivalent to human laughter is for the otter to lie on its back and wriggle while keeping its mouth wide open. Teko clearly found the result of his handiwork extremely funny.

Teko at that time was a weighty ball of very soft dark brown fur and fat and *bonhomie*; in character he was like neither Mijbil nor Edal, for he was (and still is) basically a clown. It is now nearly three years since he came to Camusfeàrna, and in that time he has grown to be the largest otter than I personally have seen, weighing perhaps fifty pounds. But his character is *au fond* unchanged, despite the two acts of violence with which his record is now stained. He has always been content to play by himself for hours at a time; in those days, when he had only a small pool, he would adapt any floatable object, a stick or an empty tin, for his water games, dragging it under water and pouncing on it as it rose again, and occasionally leaping with it on to terra firma and racing round and round the pool in circles; later, when he had a large and deep fibre-glass swimming-pool of his own, he spurned all other toys in favour of a football, and with this he elaborated techniques to which Edal had never aspired. At the beginning the basic game was to try to keep the football under water; the impossibility of this project fascinated him, and round the original theme he wove a host of variations. He would shoot out of the water like a dolphin and land upon the football, trying to bear it under with him; release it suddenly so that it shot up high in the air; stalk it from the bank and perform a thunderous belly-flopper upon it with clasping arms; dribble it round the grass enclosure using nose, four feet and tail – it was his mascot, his totem, his *alter ego*, and without it he seemed lost. His most surprising feat I should not have believed had I not witnessed it many times. The edges of the fibre-glass pool were on all sides at the top of a small bank, so that from them led down a grass declivity of two or three feet. When, therefore, his antics shot the football out of the pool, it would inevitably roll down this slope; in the early stages he was content to try to push it and manhandle it back by any means he could. This was necessarily a slow and frustrating process, and quite suddenly he discovered that he could just clasp it in his arms and walk upright on his webbed hind feet. Almost always, however, either balance or the ball would begin to slip before he reached the top of the incline, and watching him from the window one morning as this began to happen I was astonished to see him actually throw the ball up into the pool, with a swinging, upward motion of both arms.

His most popular indoor parlour trick, in those days when he was allowed to meet visitors freely, was to play with the dancing beam of a torch shone upon the floor. Finding this to be elusive, intangible to nose or paws, he seemed to conceive of his tail as possessing some magic power for the capture of will-o'-the-wisps; thus he would reverse towards the spot of light, trying to scoop at it with his tail, executing the while a quick jig step to keep pace with its movement, a highly individual step that came to be known as the *pas de loutre*.

Like Edal when she first arrived, Teko was at the outset an indifferent, barely adequate swimmer, but he lost his fears more quickly than she had done, and soon he was at home in the deepest of waters or the wildest of waves. His first day with bathers appeared utterly fascinating to him; it had not apparently crossed his mind that this curious upright foster-race who tended him could upon occasion be aquatic too. When Raef Payne, who had restored and occupied the old croft opposite to mine, accompanied him to the sea with schnorkel and flippers, Teko was wild with delighted amusement. At first he was content to dive when Raef dived, and perform intricate aquabatics around him deep under water; then he discovered that he could ride the swimmer's back and go down with him; lastly, he found that he could embarrass the human considerably by removing the schnorkel mask when it was least expected. After such a joke he would porpoise round and round the swimmer with the rhythmic grace of a ballet dancer; he seemed to laugh at his own antics and at those of all the world around him. I am glad that one coloured film was made of Teko that summer, before anyone had any cause to fear him.

Alas, Edal's only reaction to this splendid beast remained one of violent jealousy against an interloper. Like the Marquis of Montrose, her heart did evermore disdain a rival to her throne, as it was plainly as such rather than a consort that she viewed him.

Exercising the two animals separately occupied much time, and I found my writing falling sadly behind. I decided to engage a second otter keeper, and in July Terry Nutkins arrived by way, so to speak, of the London Zoo. He was not employed there, but spent much of his free time about the Elephant House; his ambition was to be a *mahout*. This project presenting patent difficulties, he was inclined to accept any employment involving the care of animals outside an urban area. He came to Camus-feàrna as Teko's keeper, and the two established immediate *rapport*.

3

Peace Dropping Slow

In the autumn of 1959, soon after the narrative of *Ring of Bright Water* had been brought to a close, my mother had undergone a serious operation in London, and it was clear that the timelessness of Camusfeàrna, its isolation from the outside world, must be regarded as an essentially egotistical aspect of my life. Camusfeàrna was a haven and a refuge, but with the necessity of spending an ever-increasing part of each year so far from responsibility came, too, the necessity for communication. I had expected the telephone to be beyond my means, brought, as it would have to be, by a separate line of posts all the weary distance from the road at Druimfiaclach; I was unfamiliar with the whimsical vagaries of the Postmaster-General's office, and the quotation of a mere five pounds installation fee I took at first sight for an unusually crass clerical error. In this I was wrong, and beyond a slightly increased rent for the instrument, the miracle was unqualified.

For some time before the installation of the actual telephone itself the effect was that of being under siege from a slowly approaching army. The advance began out of sight, far away up the hill, with a series of muffled but menacing explosions that grew daily heavier; the attackers themselves remained as yet invisible, though after the fourth day their hoarse and seemingly ferocious cries drifted down to us on the wind between distant detonations. Then one morning they were upon us; a mighty bang and a patter of falling rock-chips brought us bounding from our beds early one morning to see their heads upon the horizon three hundred yards away. They stood motionless in a group, regarding our defencelessness; one of them held before him a small uprooted birch tree.

'Birnam Wood,' I said.

'Don't worry, these people only attack at dusk.'

How often I have wished that were true of the telephone itself. The large outside bell above the door of the house jangles arrogantly at all hours, and often at what Terry Nutkins might, with unusual aptness, have termed 'the most undignified moment of the day'. Terry, never of an academic or scholastic turn of mind, had when he first arrived a limited but highly experimental vocabulary; one day I found in my typewriter the beginning of a practice business letter which read: 'Dear Sir, I received your letter on Monday at a very undignified moment of the day. I can't say that I liked the tone of your voice.' Such undignified moments were even less convenient for telephone calls at Camusfeàrna than they are in civilisation, for at that time we still had no sanitation; Moab was our washpot, and over Edom we cast out our shoes. As a factor replied to a former Duke of Argyll, visiting an outlying island of his property, 'Is it a *toilet* you're wanting, your Grace? The whole bloody *island* is a toilet!'

The first incoming telephone call was received at Camusfeàrna on April 11th 1960, and in retrospect the bell seems seldom to have been silent since. While the presence of the telephone has removed from Camusfeàrna a little of our sense of security, it has substituted another, for as a place of permanent residence it is a house of crisis, particularly in the winter; and in the frequent emergencies of human and animal health, of shipwreck and the accidents of fire and flood, there is the knowledge that help, however remote, can be summoned. Now, too, we could telephone for the household food supplies, as opposed to ordering them by letter two days in advance; it brought, in however small a quantity, relief from the exigence of a routine that left ever less time either to write or to enjoy Camusfeàrna. The next logical step towards buying back a little of the leisure I had lost by treating the house as a permanent home rather than a temporary haven, seemed the installation of electricity to take over at least a few of

34

the endless chores which kept us house-bound during long days of summer, or cold and comfortless in the twilight of winter. Like the telephone line, the power-wires also followed the roadside at Druimfiaclach; the distance was the same, and in my innocence it even appeared to me possible that the same poles might carry both lines. I knew little of departmentalism. Not only was it impossible for the North of Scotland Hydro-Electric Board to use the same poles but even to use the same route of approach. The telephone line branches to Camusfeàrna from Druimfiaclach – now I received a plan showing the proposed electrical supply starting from a full half-mile farther to the southward, and an estimate for installation into which that for the telephone would have divided nearly two hundred times. But I was determined upon it, determined to avoid the transport of ponderous calor-gas containers and paraffin drums through the winter hurricanes; in my mind, too, were shining, ill-defined images of labour-saving devices; visions of placid hours of writing uninterrupted by the recurrent oppression of household tasks undone. So there came again the distant din of an advancing army, and at length a new group reached the southern horizon and stood looking down upon us with, it seemed, a wild surmise. On July 4th a party of the raiders approached the house itself, staggering across the green field under the weight of what appeared to be an enormous battering-ram; to complete the illusion of warfare they began immediately and feverishly to dig slit-trenches. At length the battering-ram was hoisted upright and revealed itself as the feed-post to stand beside the house, the slit-trenches as recipients of vast baulks of timber to anchor its guy-wires.

When Teko was plainly settled into his new home we tried again, with all the caution born of experience, to introduce him to Edal. Some part of our difficulty lay in the fact that we did not know whether Edal had a greater affection for her keeper, Jimmy Watt, or for myself; Edal, it was clear, considered herself polyandrously married to both of us, and apparent infidelity by either of us towards another otter could touch off the full fury of a *Lutra cornuta*. The question posed itself simply as to who should lead which animal on these trial walks; nor did her behaviour do much to elucidate the problem, for she was furious if either of us led Teko, and even more furious if he stopped for a second to pick up some shell or other piece of jetsam that struck him as a desirable toy. Habituation by proximity had already proved a failure; we had constructed a small window in the wall of Teko's enclosure, a mere six inches square and formed of two thicknesses of fine-mesh wire netting two inches apart, through which they could see and smell each other but could inflict no damage. But soon we had to close this hatch in order to preserve reason. Daylong Edal would stand at the grill and with all the force contained in her small frame she projected the unearthly, ear-splitting expression of her enmity; no other sub-human sound that I know is so baring to the nerves, unless it be the screaming of a falcon that has been mishandled in transference to its foster-parents. (Falcons taken too young from the eyrie become fixated upon the humans who have removed and fed them, and will scream at the mere proximity of their foster-parents. To overcome this a 'screamer' is fed with tongs from behind a screen of sacking. Presumably, but of this I have no knowledge, the falcon will then scream at any pair of tongs crossing its vision, but there are fewer of these loose in the world than there are human beings.) But while Edal's screaming-window was an unqualified failure as a factor in her acclimatisation to Teko, I did, as the weeks passed, begin to entertain some small hope for their future; when exercised together on leashes her attention was not so perpetually concentrated upon him, nor, when Jimmy and I separated and unleashed our respective otters, did she seem so keenly inclined to pursue Teko and put him to rout.

Then, early in August, all experiments stopped together, for it became not a question of whether we could save this situation but, for the second time that year, whether we could save Edal's life. Edal, who had for so long played marbles on the kitchen floor, slept on our pillows, and displayed all the intense affection of which an otter is capable, developed an infection of the brain arising from a septic tooth. In twenty-four hours she became a mad,

36

savage, half-paralysed but unapproachable creature, recognising no one, as dangerous as a wounded leopard yet to me as pathetic as a child mortally sick. I can still see her crazed head weaving in search of something to attack, her useless hindquarters dragging behind her before she would collapse in a twitching rigor. Perhaps I may not be blamed too much for having hoped that each of these might be the end of an animal that now bore no resemblance to Edal.

It had started, as I have said, with a septic tooth, and as soon as we saw that she was in pain we arranged to have the tooth extracted on the following day. This involved taking her by car to a far-distant town, and, as always upon such emergency occasions, the next day was a Sunday. The vet was, however, prepared to perform the operation at any time, and we arranged by telephone that Edal should be at his surgery by eleven o'clock in the morning. (A long succession of crises such as this and worse than this have made me wonder how Camusfeàrna was ever supportable without the telephone; Parkinson's Law that expenditure rises to meet income may evidently be extended to the theorem that crises rise to meet communication.)

Early in the morning we set off up the hill on foot, for there is no road to Camusfeàrna. At this stage Edal seemed normal, though once or twice it struck me fleetingly that there were moments when she found balance difficult. This suggested to me a derangement of her cerebellum, the hind part of the brain responsible for controlling movement, and with my limited knowledge it appeared no more than sensible to take some precaution against a similar disturbance of the cerebrum, the fore-brain controlling behaviour. I insisted, therefore, that Jimmy, in whose charge she would be while I drove, should wear thick gloves.

The car was a hard-top Land Rover, with a full division between front and rear. We had not as yet any precise reason to be afraid of her, and with a sheepskin coat we made for her a bed on the centre seat of the front cab, so that she was between us. Trouble started within the first half mile. Without any warning she flew at Jimmy's hands, and had they not been heavily gloved the damage would have been great. Again and again she repeated these attacks, and I thought my own ungloved hands would be her next target, for she seemed to resent movement, and I had to reach directly in front of her in order to use the gear lever. But in her confused brain it was Jimmy that she hated at that moment, and she treated me as if I did not exist. After three miles of acute nervous tension it became plain that the situation was untenable, and that one or other of us would be seriously hurt long before we had completed the eighty miles in front of us.

In her present condition it was not easy to see how to transfer her to the rear compartment, much less close the door upon her. We had to dangle her down out of the front cab on the end of her lead, taking care all the while that she could not come within range of us, and then to hoist her over the rear drop-board, a very much more difficult procedure. When, after some ten minutes of effort, we had at last completed the task and closed the door upon her, we argued that her behaviour might in fact be no more than the effect of the tranquillisers we had given her before we started; they had, it is true, been of a variety that we had not tried before, but in all my previous experience tranquillisers administered to otters had produced the reverse of the desired and expected effect. They seemed to act much as alcohol affects the majority of human beings, leading to breakdown of all inhibitions and the collapse of learned behaviour; a wild animal in acute pain and without inhibitions could hardly be expected to display tranquillity and good humour.

At the surgery, two hours later, we were confronted with fresh difficulties, for there was no anaesthetic chamber, and we were forced to improvise with a large tea-chest. Into this we lowered her as we had lowered her into the rear compartment of the Land Rover, and then air-sealed the top with heavy towels before pumping in the anaesthetic. Edal took what was for me an almost intolerable time to lose consciousness, for all the while she wailed like a wounded hare, a sound so utterly piteous and abandoned that I found my hands unsteady and a cold sweat coming out on my forehead. Jimmy was unable to bear it, and took refuge in the Land Rover outside.

When at last these dreadful cries had ceased we removed the towels and lifted her limp body out of the box and on to the operating table. Two vets worked upon her, but found it impossible to shift the molar. No ordinary practitioner could be expected to know the precise jaw and skull structure of an otter, much less of a foreign species; this tooth resisted every normal means of extraction, and, not knowing how high the roots were planted in the skull, they were afraid of inflicting fatal damage if they used greater force. Seeing Edal lying there limp upon the operating table, her mouth full of blood and her fur foul with her own excreta, I did not believe in her recovery. The one slender chance was that the mauling the tooth had received might have provided some drainage for the septic fluids.

We carried her back into the Land Rover no more than seconds before she came round from the anaesthetic; through the rear window I could see her, dazed and bloodstained, walking round and round the narrow floor space in stumbling circles. The part of me that remains a child was very near to tears.

At the end of the two-hour journey home I felt a small spark of hope, for she was able to walk down the hill, and though she was noticeably off balance I supposed this to be the after-effects of the anaesthetic. She would not eat, but in the circumstances this seemed no great cause for surprise. We contrived, again by dangling her from the end of a lead, to hoist her upstairs into her own quarters; there she appeared to go to sleep in her bed, and we left her for the night.

Early the next morning Mr Donald MacLennan, the local vet, came – I use the word local for want of a better, for he lives at Broadford in Skye, more than fifty miles away by road and sea-ferry. I was totally unprepared for the rapid overnight deterioration in Edal's condition, and I opened her door to bring her downstairs. She was partially paralysed and wholly mad. She fell rather than walked down the stairs, and stumbled out into the garden, where she toppled over on her side, kicking and twitching. I took this first convulsion for a death-agony, but after perhaps a minute she recovered from it, raised herself unsteadily, and looked around her with mad eyes for something to attack.

Finally, for despite the paralysis she seemed enormously strong, she struggled into the living-room and dragged herself up into a low wooden armchair with a slot back. Here she was unapproachable, screaming and literally gnashing her teeth at the least sign of movement in the room.

The vet looked at her and said nothing; I was unused then to the painstaking deliberation of his diagnoses, and I took his silence for a death-warrant. Yet I did not want him to shoulder the responsibility; I knew that in a month's time, when *Ring of Bright Water* was to be published, Edal would become a famous animal, more famous, perhaps than Elsa the Lioness, and I felt it unfair to this young man to leave the decision to him alone. I telephoned to London, and the advice I received was unequivocal. Had I got a gun in the house? I had a pistol and only one remaining round; I searched for it and found it before returning to the living-room. It seemed to me now only a question of how Edal's execution could be carried out with the least possible distress to herself and to the humans who had made a pet of her. But the young vet, with his soft, deliberate Highland speech, said: 'It is not fair to consult a practitioner six hundred miles from the patient; he is not on the spot, and he has no opportunity to form an opinion as he would like. A bullet will prove nothing, and also it would spoil the body for post-mortem. I think there is a very faint chance, and if you are willing to try I am. We shall have to give her very massive injections of antibiotics daily for five days, and if there is no improvement then she will go into a coma and die quietly.' I felt, and I expect looked, helpless; I could not see how we might approach Edal closely enough to touch her, let alone restrain and inject her.

We had one small help – the slotted back to the chair on which she was sitting. While I distracted her attention from the front, Jimmy contrived somehow to clip a lead on to her harness through the gaps in the woodwork. Then, by using a shepherd's crook, I managed to lift the lead through until it was on the same side of the chair-back as she was. Down this lead we slipped the hand loop of another, so that she could be held from two different directions; in this way we moved her slowly off the chair until we could take a turn of one lead round a table leg. Then we drew the other lead tight too, from a direction at right-angles to the first, and I took hold of her tail. Even when she was held from three points and could not turn her head she managed to lash her body like a wounded snake. It must have been little easier than injecting a flying bird, but that vet did it, as I was to see him do it so often in the future. Then we put on rubber thigh-boots, and half hoisted, half dangled her back upstairs and into her own room, leaving attached to her the two leads that would make further injections possible.

For the following four days we repeated the same procedure, and each day Donald MacLennan showed the same extraordinary legerdemain in injecting his moving target. We entered that room only in thigh-boots – we did not know then how little protection these would have offered had Edal reached and attacked us with purpose – and always as we went about the daily routine of cleaning the floor and changing her water she would drag her paralysed hindquarters after her in pathetic attempts to attack.

Then at last came a day when as I entered the room I seemed to sense something different in her appearance. She was curled up in her bed in the corner, so that only her head protruded from the blankets, and she seemed to look at me questioningly, as though I had been away for a long time and she was not sure whether it could be me. I came nearer to her, and suddenly she gave a little whimper of recognition as she had been used to when she was pleased to see Jimmy or myself. With great hesitation I gave her the back of my bare hand to sniff, and the greeting sounds redoubled. I knew then that, however long her physical paralysis might remain, she was now mentally normal. I knelt down on the floor beside her and put my face down to her and stroked her, and she rubbed her whiskers over my cheeks and pushed her nose into my neck while all the time she whimpered her welcome and affection for someone who had been away for so long.

Physically, her convalescence and recovery were protracted, but they progressed in precisely the sequence that the vet had hoped for; a returning power in her fore-quarters, then her hind limbs and, last of all, the ability to move her tail. It was early

October before I was able to take her out of the house for the first time; that she had locomotive power was all that could be said, for her movements were awkward and ill-coordinated, each front foot raised high on the forward pace as if she were striking at something, and even in the hundred yards or so that I took her she lay down several times with a look of bewilderment and despair on her face. Very slowly, over a period of months, she regained the full use of all her muscles, began to play again, and to gallop and swim and dive. One day early in November I found her playing on the floor with a new toy that she had some-where discovered; it was the single round of pistol ammunition with which I had been about to end her life on August 8th 1960.

The little seaside village four miles from Camusfeàrna had its own disciple of McGonagall, a small, sandy-haired man, at that time still under thirty. He is known as the Bard, and few local events of any significance escape celebration by his pen. It was therefore to be expected that the death at the hands of Big Angus of my first otter Mijbil, with its many repercussions in the neighbour-hood, would have drawn from him some prolonged utterance. I did, in fact, know of the existence of this ballad, but I had never heard it nor read it. The Bard was, indeed, only the barest of acquaintances.

Late one dark Saturday evening he and a friend of his own age, Duncan from the Isle of Skye, knocked at Camusfeàrna door. They explained that they had been mackerel fishing with an out-board dinghy, and had found themselves so near to Camusfeàrna Lighthouse that the Bard had decided to call upon us and recite his ballad. He was profusely and repetitively apologetic for his friend who, he said, had taken just a very little too much to drink in the pub before they had set out – not much too much, you will understand, but just enough to make the sensitive Bard feel apologies to be required. We brushed these to one side and led the two to the living-room; there it was clear that the friend was indeed lightly and happily inebriated, not in such a degree as to affect his always excellent manners, but enough to dim his con-sonants. The Bard's eye was but slightly glassy and his speech was

42

perfect; only the insistence of his repeated apologies for Duncan's lapse of taste in visiting me in his present condition might have led one to suspect that Duncan had not been drinking alone.

With characteristic generosity of spirit they had brought their own whisky with them, and insisted upon providing the first round before they would drink any of my own. This is an excellent and well-tried Highland device for the production of a long and convivial session; the host must always offer one for the road, or in this case the sea, and the guest will always be offended if the host does not accept one in return. It is the perfect formula for oblivion, and quite early on in the evening I began to feel the probability that the Bard and his friend would pass the night at Camusfeàrna. After an hour or so I thought it might be as well to hear the ballad while the going was good, but the Bard turned suddenly coy, and boisterous bullying from Duncan only produced from him further earnest and insistent apologies for his friend's deplorable state. The Bard was still making interesting and intelligent conversation, and it seemed to me that he was perhaps insufficiently primed for public recitation; I filled their glasses again. As the evening wore on a subtle and curious shift of balance began to take place between Duncan and the Bard; the more Duncan drank the more sober he appeared to become, and the more the Bard drank the more he became patently drunk. By midnight the roles had become completely reversed; now it was Duncan, apparently as sober as a judge, who repeatedly apologised for the Bard and rebuked him for his gross behaviour, while the Bard's speech thickened to the point of inarticulacy and he became increasingly unsteady on his feet.

It was at about this point that he considered the time ripe for recitation of the ballad. Calling for total silence he climbed precariously to his feet and stood swaying like a tree in a high wind. Had he allowed himself support even with one hand on chimney-piece or chair-back, the occasion might still have been carried off, but it was the Bard's habit to deliver himself of his verses while standing rigidly to attention, and this position is notoriously difficult at any time after the first dozen whiskies. In the circumstances he did quite creditably to get through the first few lines, though my attention was distracted from them by the obvious imminence of disaster.

A wilder sway than any before canted the Bard backward at an angle from which there could be no recovery, and he toppled over with a tremendous crash into the wood basket, his music still within him. There he lay sprawling, replete, all interest in recitation gone, resisting any effort to set him upright again, clearly completely content where he was. We conferred with Duncan, who the while drank another glass of whisky to complete his sobering-up.

He was brisk and competent. We decided that we should have to carry the Bard to the dinghy in which he had arrived, which was not in the bay below the house but several hundred yards away at the mouth of the river. Outside, it proved to be one of those pitch-black nights without a single star visible in the sky, a night when even the calm surface of the sea gave back no reflection from above. Carrying electric torches, we transported the Bard stumblingly through the sand-dunes and over the steep shingle to the dinghy, the entire floorboards of which were covered in a layer of mackerel some six inches deep. With care and difficulty we sat him upon the front thwart; it was solicitude wasted, for he immediately slithered down among the fish and lay slimily at full length upon them and among them. Hauled into a sitting position again he at once collapsed anew by simple force of gravity; eventually Duncan decided to leave him in his prone position and concentrate upon starting the outboard engine. This took some considerable time, and when at length it did start Duncan remembered that he was unfamiliar with the reefs and the islands, and stopped it again in order to ask me for directions. The whole situation appearing to me precarious, and the Bard plainly unable to be of service to himself or others in the case of shipwreck, I played for safety, telling him to keep straight on down the bay until Camusfeàrna Lighthouse was on his starboard quarter before turning north to pass the light. This time the engine was more refractory, and it was another quarter of an hour before the dinghy finally chugged off into the darkness.

We stood listening to the direction of the engine sound, anxious to be certain that he was following a safe course. After some minutes I had just said to Jimmy: 'I had no idea he had to go that far to get Camusfeàrna Lighthouse on his starboard quarter', when the engine suddenly stopped. It was a night so still that the least sound came from far across the water almost as though amplified; we listened for a long time to the recurrent stutter of the pull-starter, punctuated by an occasional oath, while the engine remained lifeless. Then Duncan seemed to abandon the attempt and turn his attention to the Bard unconscious among the mackerel. '*Wake* up, Johnnie! Wake *up*, Johnnie, can't you!' *Slap*. '*Wake up, Johnnie!*' *Slap*. ('Do you know, I believe he's slapping him with a fish?') 'For f—'s sake WAKE UP!' *Slap, slap*. No answering voice, not even a groan, and presently the whirring stutter of the starter began again. Jimmy and I were debating whether in all humanity we should not take a dinghy out and bring them back to Camusfeàrna ('the Bard will be pretty fishy by now') when quite suddenly the engine was away with a roar. We listened until the direction of the sound showed that the boat was past all immediate hazards, and we went home to bed.

Somewhere among all those fish there must have been concealed another bottle of whisky; either that or some curious chemical constituent of Duncan's blood caused alcohol to have upon him a long delayed and violent action, for next morning, the rigidly Calvinistic Sabbath morning of a West Highland village, a terrible sight was revealed to the scandalised eyes of the population. Tied up to the end of the village pier was a dinghy and, prostrate and pillowed deep among the mackerel it contained were the blissfully unconscious forms of Duncan and the Bard.

It was not until long after this that I learned from the Bard that the text of the ballad that had been so tantalisingly cut short in recitation was lost for ever.

Not all Saturday evening visitors were as unproductive of recitation or of anecdote as was the Bard. My nearest nighbour, Calum Murdo MacKinnon, would often spend an evening at Camusfeàrna, and he is a talented raconteur of considerable repertoire, knowing any tale ancient and modern, sacred and profane, of the scattered local communities. One such evening, I remember, he devoted with much relish to the saga of a certain Dugalt, a bygone hero who in character and activity resembled nothing so much as an aboriginal Basil Seal, tormenting his fellows not only for his own needs and diversion, but almost with a sense of dedication. This archetypal trickster coloured his mischievous and predatory pranks with a rich hue of mockery, and an aura of success, for allied to his hare-brained approach to existence were a keen mind and a rumbustious sense of farce. He was, needless to say, without profession, travelling widely in Northern Scotland and living by his wits and his ever-increasing local knowledge.

He entered, and immediately monopolised the conversation at Camusfeàrna that evening, because we had been discussing a subject of perennial importance to an otter-keeping household, the prices of fish. The current cost of cod in our small local ports reminded Calum Murdo of a record figure once obtained by Dugalt for a medium-sized cod. Dugalt's peripatetic existence had at the time in question led him to Portree in the Isle of Skye and tied up to the pier there, he noticed a fishing boat in whose hold was a heavy catch of cod. He went aboard and began to examine these fish with an expert eye, rummaging about among them and turning them over busily; the crew, who knew his reputation for violence and invincibility too well to interfere, looked on in silence. At length he selected the largest of all the fish, and asked the boat's skipper if he might borrow it for an hour. The value of this cod would have been, say, five or six shillings, but fear of some such reprisal as had earned Dugalt's fame made the skipper accept the curious proposition without demur.

Armed with the cod, Dugalt set off into the township and knocked on the door of the first prosperous-looking house he found. Here he offered the obviously fresh and prime fish to the housewife for one shilling. She accepted with alacrity, supposing, perhaps, that the ridiculously low figure was due either to Dugalt's urgent need for alcohol or to dubious ownership of the wares he offered. Handing him the coin, she was about to take the fish from his hands when Dugalt remarked that a fine lady like her would not be wanting to soil her hands with gutting and scraping out the creature, and that as she hadn't argued about the price he would take it down to the sea and do the job for her. The delighted housewife gave him another sixpence out of the goodness of her heart and he made off towards the beach. As soon as he was out of sight of the house he turned briskly up another street that led away from the sea. Halfway up it he found another likely-looking house and sold the cod again on the same terms and with the same result. At the end of an hour, when he had sold the borrowed fish fourteen times, and collected a little over £1, he returned to the fishing boat. Throwing the cod contemptuously among the crew he called out: 'If the rest of your cod catch make the price this bugger did you've got a gold-mine down there.'

This tale whetted my appetite to learn more of the exploits of Dugalt, and soon Calum Murdo was in full swing. Dugalt, he explained, not only never paid for anything, he never even exposed himself to the risk of doing so, and to this unswerving lifelong purpose he called into play every scrap of local knowledge he could amass. He would listen seemingly without interest to local gossip in the villages he passed through, storing away for future use any scrap of information that might be of use to him in some outrage as yet unplanned. Calum Murdo went on to provide an example of how he would use a combination of brains and knowledge for ends no more ambitious than the achievement of a free meal.

Dugalt called at a lonely, outlying moorland croft, about whose occupants he had mentally filed away some fact overheard, and asked for a meal. The woman of the house was not unkindly, but she was clearly harassed and distressed, explaining that with a sick husband to nurse and all the work of the croft to do single-handed she had no time to cook for anyone else. Her man was not old, she said, but for some time past he had appeared to be ailing and unfit for heavy work; now he was unable to do a hand's turn, and for much of the time was unable even to rise from his bed. 'It's worse than having a baby to look after,' she summed up,

47

'because poor John keeps me on the run for something or other the day long.'

'Give me a good square meal,' said Dugalt, 'and I'll cure John for you. I know more than a little of medicine.'

'Well,' she replied, 'that would be worth a lot more than the price of any meal, so I'll cook you what I've got, if you'll do what you can for the poor soul.'

John lay in a box-bed at the other side of the small room, glaring malevolently at Dugalt as he ate largely and at length of all that the house could provide. At length he sat back replete, wiped his lips, and announced that it was time he moved on. 'But,' cried the housewife in dismay, 'you promised to cure my husband!' 'Did I now?' said Dugalt blandly. 'So I did, so I did. Oh dear yes, so I did, and I must keep my word. Now would you be having such a beast as a cow about the place at all?' Yes, replied the housewife, she had a cow, the best cow in all the country. 'Well,' said Dugalt, 'I know fine just to look at John what it is that ails him, and there is only one cure for it. We must kill that cow at once, skin her, and wrap John up in the bloody hide while it's still warm. Then we make a kind of paste out of whatever dung is in the gut and apply it thickly to his neck and head, and then——'

Dugalt's prescription was cut short as John sprang from the bed with a roar of rage. 'You son of the devil! You *picht*!' he yelled, and seizing up a poker he rushed at Dugalt. Dugalt dodged him nimbly, and as he skipped lightly through the door he called back over his shoulder: 'Now you've got him going, keep him on the move! I told you I knew what ailed him, and I cured him like I said I would!'

Not a few of Dugalt's efforts to keep himself at the expense of others and in the comfort to which he felt himself entitled led to minor vendettas; in these he was, of course, the invariable victor. One such war he carried on for years against a minister of the Church of Scotland, and it had as its origin nothing more momentous than Dugalt's attempt to secure himself a comfortable bed for the night. It all began one frosty winter's night when Dugalt came knocking at the manse door at 2 a.m. The minister heard the knocking, but, hoping that his housekeeper would hear and answer, he pulled the bedclothes over his head and paid no heed. The knocking persisted. At length, reflecting that it would be unseemly to go to the housekeeper's room at that hour of night, and determined to be rid of this nuisance at any cost, the minister descended and opened the door himself. It was the first of his many meetings with Dugalt, and he acted as he would have done to any other tramp, with no suspicions of his visitor's special attributes. Dugalt asked for a bed, and the minister replied that he was welcome to sleep in the loft, where there was plenty of hay to provide a soft mattress. He even went further in his Christian spirit, and brought Dugalt a ladder, placing it for him against the entrance to the loft. It was very dark. Dugalt commented upon this, adding that as his eyesight was poor at the best of times the minister would be doing him a great service if he would ascend first and stretch down a reassuring hand to guide him into the loft. Longing to be rid of his visitor and to return to his warm bed, the minister acquiesced and began to climb the ladder. 'Be sure and call down to me when you're in the loft, Minister,' said Dugalt, 'and then I'll know you're steadying the top of the ladder for me before I start going up.' Presently the minister announced that he was kneeling on the loft floor and holding the ladder steady. With a quick wrench Dugalt twisted it from his hands and lowered it carefully to the ground. 'If the bed up there's so comfortable, Minister, I'll let you be taking it yourself and I'll use your hard one in-by the house.' Entering the manse by the still open front door, he had little difficulty in locating the minister's bedroom and there he curled up comfortably between good linen sheets.

When the housekeeper got up in the morning she found Dugalt sitting demurely in the kitchen. He had, he said, a message from the minister – she would please cook Dugalt breakfast, and not just porridge or suchlike but a proper breakfast with bacon and eggs. The housekeeper, never of even temper, said she would take no such messages. 'Then,' retorted Dugalt, 'just you go and ask him yourself if what I say's not true.' 'I will that,' she said, and stumped up to the minister's bedroom. She returned in puzzlement some minutes later, to enquire when and where Dugalt had last seen the minister. 'Well,' said Dugalt, 'seeing you're his own housekeeper and will wish him no ill, I'll tell you the truth. He had me bring him Bessie Allison [the local tart] a bit after midnight and they spent the night in the hayloft together. Well, I'm sure you'll not blame the poor body, and I must be on my way now.' By midday he was plotting fresh mischief in a village ten miles away.

This was the first skirmish of what became a prolonged persecution by Dugalt of the minister, who was not, in fact, an unworthy adversary. In the days before his ordination he had been far from holy; he had been a boozer and a fighter, and because he was a man of huge stature and violent nature he had been a figure of fear. His conversion when it had come had been complete and uncompromising. Upon his ordination he had become a veritable tower of Calvinism, and a hell-fire preacher. At first, in the rough highland parish which had been his first charge, there had been few to listen to his ferocious sermons, for his predecessor was a weak man who had lost his congregation, and the rougher element of the district was determined that the new minister should not regain it. They were, however, unfamiliar with his history. On the second Sunday that he preached to the small handful of faithful, he found as he left the church that his way was barred by a crowd of young hooligans. Their leader, a massive youth with cold blue eyes and tow-coloured hair, came forward until he was within touching distance of the minister. 'Minister,' he said, 'it is written that if a man smite thee on the cheek thou shalt turn the other,' and with all his strength he swung his fist at the minister's cheek. He might as well have struck the solid rock of Scotland. The minister neither moved nor flinched. 'It is also written,' he remarked calmly, 'that such measure as is meted out to you shall ye mete out again,' and his fist swung up in a long slicing upper-cut that lifted the young man clean off his feet and laid him unconscious on the grass. The minister looked round at the others. 'And that's what you'll all get if you try that game with me,' he added as he bent and hauled their leader to his feet with a hand twisting his collar. He did more than haul him to his feet, for within an hour he had him and all his gang inside the church, and within a month had secured them, either by fear or by admiration, as permanent members of his congregation.

Now in due course Dugalt heard that it was none other than this formidable man of God upon whom he had played his prank in the hayloft, and curiosity drew him back to the village to hear one of the sulphurous sermons that were so widely talked of. It was thus that one Sabbath morning the minister perceived with some alarm the presence of Dugalt in one of the hinder pews of his church. For a short time Dugalt, to whom a church service held all the attraction of novelty, found himself almost interested by it all, and almost impressed despite himself by the fire of the minister's voice. But gradually his attention began to wander, and as it wandered he became bored, a condition which he was never prepared to tolerate for long. He looked around him in search of diversion.

In those days it was customary for the hill shepherds to bring their collie dogs to church; the shepherds would occupy the rear pews, and it was among them and some twenty or more dogs, that Dugalt now found himself. The dogs, he decided, were the possible raw material of pandemonium. He had some bread and cheese in his pocket, and this he began furtively to toss to the dogs, singling out for his favours those that seemed most thrawn in appearance. At the end of no more than a couple of minutes he had started a dog-fight, and the minister's words were drowned in a demoniac babel of yelping, snarling canine voices. Under the pretext of trying to separate the snapping mass of combatants Dugalt waded into them, kicking and throwing into the fight any who had so far escaped involvement. The mighty voice of the minister rose above the din in a great Gaelic bellow of anguish and despair, 'PUT OUT THAT FOOL! PUT OUT THAT FOOL!' to which Dugalt roared back above the sounds of battle, 'FHIRNACRANNAIG CHEID MI FHEINAMACH!' (literally, 'I'll go out myself, fellow of the churn!' – a reference to the resemblance between the pulpits and the milk churns of olden times.) He flounced out, slamming the door behind him, and when, after some painful minutes, order had been restored in the body of the church the ruffled and fuming minister addressed himself to his sermon. He still under-estimated his opponent.

Once outside the church Dugalt looked round him in search of further entertainment. The first thing he noticed was that the key of the church door was in its lock, so as a preliminary to any further activity he turned it securely and put it in his pocket. He was now thoroughly enjoying himself, and beginning once again to bubble over with inventive mischief. Outside the church he noted a gig, the horse grazing on tether; he also noted the convenient placement of the church bellrope used for summoning the faithful to prayer. He connected horse and slack bellrope firmly together, tied the key of the church door to the horse's halter, and retired to a concealed vantage point to await developments. The horse grazed peacefully away until it reached a point at which the bellrope tightened and the bell began to toll; the horse started and flung up his head, and the bell jangled louder and more wildly. The horse sensed the connection between his own movements and these sounds that seemed directed at him, and began to back and to plunge and to rear, and the more he did so the louder and more feverishly the bell clanged. Above its din came the sound of shouting and hammering within the church door. It was a door built sturdily and uncompromisingly, as befitted the God worshipped beyond it; there was no possible way out but the window high in the wall beyond the pulpit. One by one the whole congregation, young and old, lean and stout, sylph-like maidens and balloon-like matrons, shepherds and dogs, made their painful and undignified exit to land sprawling in the grass. Dugalt is said to have rated this exploit high in his annals of outrage, considering that he had made the best possible use of all materials and opportunities to hand.

The incident had, however, in no way satiated his appetite for baiting this aggressive man of God; it served, on the contrary, as a stimulus to further planning, for the minister had preached against Dugalt from the pulpit. His opportunity came later that summer. The minister had a large glebe (the piece of land that is attached to the manse or residence of a minister of the Church of Scotland), and in the year in question he had grown upon the glebe a particularly fine crop of corn. There had long been a disputed right of way across this patch of ground, and as the corn began to ripen the congregation of a rival church began, not unprompted by Dugalt, to exert their supposed right of passage across it. Fearful of the minister's reputation with his fists, they confined their activities to the dark hours or to such times as he was known to be absent, and he had not been able to lay his hands upon a single one of his opponents. Frustrated from physical and satisfying methods of deterrence, he had erected *Trespassers Will Be Prosecuted* notices, and now made it his custom to patrol the property from dusk until a full hour after dark. A lesser man than Dugalt would have considered that his plan to make the minister's life a misery had already succeeded admirably, but Dugalt was an artist, and insisted always upon a full dramatic climax to every episode. The presence of the minister in the cornfield after dark gave him opportunity to display his full virtuosity of technique.

Choosing a night that was neither too light nor too dark for his purpose, he armed himself with a heavy stick and set off stealthily for the glebe. Prospecting carefully from its perimeter, he could just make out the figure of the minister standing in a line of corn flattened by the feet of his rival congregation. Dugalt watched him patrol up and down this strip, and manoeuvred himself into a position at which the outermost point of the minister's beat would bring him to within a few yards of the watcher. Here he waited. At the next approach of the sentry, Dugalt leapt out upon him with a roar, beating him with his stick and yelling, 'Caught you at last, you bugger! You good for nothing trespasser! you *evil* person – trampling the corn of the man of God! How dare you spoil the minister's crop! I'll teach you to set yourself up against a holy man! If he was here himself he'd give you worse than this!' Through the yells and the whacks came the minister's distraught and pleading voice as he tried to ward off the rain of blows. 'It's *me*! I *am* the minister! I'm on my own ground!' but Dugalt affected to hear nothing, and the minister, caught totally unprepared, had no option but to take to his heels. As he ran for the house Dugalt pursued at his tail, beating him about the back and buttocks and screeching his denunciation. Only when the minister reached the manse and slammed the door in his face did he stop, and said in a loud, reflective stage-voice: 'This is the manse. I wonder if that could have been the minister himself, poor soul.'

THE CIRCULATION OF LIGHT

Child after child, as time disposes,
Comes crying down to the blind mazes,
And, with this world, puts on a pelt,
The wolfskin of ancestral guilt.
As if for clarity was needed
A creature on all fours and blinded,
And prerequisite, such a night,
For the beatitudes of light.

Some catch no gleam though; doom, it jars
Their wincing ghost, the manias
Hedged round about them are too thick
For the slim verities of shock
To pierce. Transfixed, till time erases
The beating life of its gross mazes,
Wait they, bereft of wrong and right,
The circulation of the light.

By energies foregone and banished,
By just so much are we diminished,
And yet it is by shades out-thrown
From what we are we can be known,
If we take back from the dark mirror
Of someone else, both love and terror;
Initiate so, by second sight,
The circulation of the light.

Here and today, past time it glosses
With a bad cloud the human faces,
And men, their real need and hunger,
Are blurred for me by some past anger,
Dreams that still colour and work on
My time, long past their origin
In those whose life my life possessed;
Rid me, I say, of this foul taste!
But still it breaks through day and night,
The circulation of the light.

THOMAS BLACKBURN

4

Some Past Anger

A LITTLE before Christmas 1960 I left Camusfeàrna for North Africa. Jimmy and Terry were in charge of the otters, and a friend who wanted sanctuary in which to write of an expedition from which he had recently returned had undertaken to run the household and deal with any emergency that might arise. I knew that I should not see Camusfeàrna again for several months.

I passed the winter and the spring in Morocco, Tunisia and Algeria; as week succeeded week my curiosity in the strange, dark unfolding of North African Arab destiny crumbled. Yet I could not leave. I became as a sleepwalker or as one in a hypnotic state, in a state of mental and physical confusion, living in an evil dream from which I found it impossible to awake. I grew weak with dysentery, and towards the end it was only with the greatest of effort that I could stir myself to complete the necessary routine of the day. Clinically, I recognised symptoms I had seen in others; they were those of multiple division of aim, for I no longer knew why I was there. Once I thought that I should write a book about those months, and I even knew the title, *The Haywire Winter*. But now I think that I never shall, and this chapter will, mercifully, be all that remains of it. The images that come back to me now are those of March and April, when my ill-health, lethargy and depression were at their greatest, and they are for the most part of two rooms several hundred miles apart.

One of them is, I suppose, within spitting distance of a real street, a shoddy street, but complete with all the properties of an intermediate civilisation. There are shops selling ironmongery, radios and bicycles. There is nothing exotic about the street but for the people who promenade its length; Berbers from the mountains, in coarse woollen *djellebahs* with the silver dagger slung under the left armpit; turbaned negroes from an ancient race of slaves; bearded and black-capped Jews from the Mellah; a host of tattered beggars. That was my street; even then I do not think I knew its name, for it is nowhere written unless on some town plan. From it lead alleys, perhaps six foot wide, of beaten earth with high solid-seeming mud walls, the infinite, bewildering alleys of an Arab town. In them are the smells of spice, ordure, charcoal-cooking, human beings and impregnated dust. In daylight the narrow view of the sky above is blank and blue, anonymous; at night the stars show as a studded belt of diamonds on dark velvet.

The room in which I lived belonged to, but was not part of, an Arab hotel; its entrance a few yards down a dust alley, a few hundred years away from the street outside. At the entrance to the alley, a stone bollard blocks entrance to wheeled vehicles; small children play leap-frog on the bollard but not over the dividing years. The hotel has a door of faded, once-gaudy paintwork and wrought-iron tracery. Beyond the door lies a square, tiled courtyard and a wealth of heavy vegetation. More precisely, there were four banana trees, growing from the four corners of a pool made sinister either by association or by its inmates. When I first knew the courtyard the trees, whose giant leaves, withered brown at their edges, invade the whole rectangle of the gallery above, grew from concrete containers painted in a brilliant shade of blue; but the roots pressed outward and split them, and the paint has flaked away from the concrete. One tree stands, unclothed, so to speak, from the waist down, and the soil has fallen from between the naked roots. At another corner a tree has gone while its concrete container remains; there is a little bed of earth there, and some small, hesitant verdure competes, unsuccessfully, with dusty razor blades and the butt-ends of cigarettes. Razor blades lie, too, at the floor of the pool, which has lost its splendour. I do not know the species of the fish that inhabit it; there are perhaps two dozen of them, some muddy brown and some red.

Like the hotel, they are sickly: one is encrusted with erupting boils, white and diseased upon the red scales. Perhaps this disfigurement was caused by the cat (there were two, but one died of typhus, vomiting out all that was left of its digestive system from the gallery into the patio below) who crouches on the crumbling concrete and swipes with clumsy, amateurish zeal at any fish within reach. As far as I knew, the cat had never actually caught a fish, just as no one had actually destroyed the hotel, but everything was dying of a mortal sickness.

I lived in the hotel's *garçonnière* which was not, by any standards, an ideal residence, and for which I paid five shillings a day. A vast but uncomplicated key turns three times to open its door, beyond which mounts a steep and ruinous stairway in total darkness, for the lights do not work. My room itself is high, bleak and decaying; there is never enough light by which to read, for only a single weak bulb dangles from the remote ceiling. There is a damaged wardrobe, a table with one leg missing, a chair and a bed; there is no covering to the floor, and on the walls are obscene grafitti. At moments this room appeared the limit of my world.

From this room led another containing a wash-basin, a lavatory and a bath, but the water system had been long defunct. A trickle of cold water could be extracted from the bath tap; this would eject from the waste-pipe a scurrying mass of big brown cockroaches, then a greenish slime would rise slowly and remain, for no water could escape from the bath.

As the image of that place returns to me now it is at evening towards the close of Ramadan. The voices of the beggars reach crescendo, for they must collect enough coins with which to eat before, at sundown, the siren sounds the close of the fast for the day. Directly under my window, at one side of the alley entrance, stands a blind beggar in a tattered *djellebah*. His right hand is outstretched, his left cupping his elbow; his head is laid slightly to one side, and he wears what one might take at first sight to be a self-deprecatory grin, as though he were an important person in fancy dress, doing this to accede to the whim of someone else. Twenty-five times a minute, for hours on end by day and by night, he calls at lung-pitch '*Allah!*' Five paces from him at the other side of the alley entrance, squats another, the hood of his *djellebah* fallen forward over his face (mercifully, for he has neither eyes nor nose). He is not content with so simple a supplication; he shouts a whole sentence of five complex words that are meaningless to me. There is an interval of five seconds between each repetition, an interval so precise that he must count. There can be little else to do inside that dark, muffled world where the only reality is the touch of coin on palm.

A few paces again from him squats a woman, still young and veiled despite the humiliation of her condition. On and around her lap crouch at least three (sometimes it seemed to me to be many more) small children, all, one would have said, below the age of three. They move and squirm and whimper among the folds of her clothing like a litter of blind puppies; their mother, if it is she, rocks from side to side as though in anguish, and her continual plaint is wild and high as the keening of jackals. The little ones are learning to speak; they are being taught the beggar's whine and the imploring gesture. At the sight of a likely looking passer-by the woman will nudge one of them, and, as if by doing so she sets in motion some ill-regulated clockwork machine, some one of her litter will disentangle its little limbs to stretch out a hand as small as a monkey's and set up a ready wail in imitation of her own. If the child does not respond she will pinch it until it cries in earnest.

There are other beggars whose voices reach me, none the less insistent for their greater distance, and beyond their continuous plaint comes the steady rhythm of drums and cymbals. The tops of the snow-covered mountains catch the last of the sun as it slants down into the Atlantic; above the palms and the minarets the homing flights of white egrets are at first still pale against the sky, then they become darker and the late stragglers change to silhouette. Two hooded figures squat in the dust of the alley outside my door, slitting the throats of chickens over a small drain; there is a terrible commotion from the dying wings as the knife cuts through each neck. The dusk soaks up the blood slowly, cats paw at it petulantly and lick their toes. One evening at the close of Ramadan . . .

59

The siren shrills high and thin, a violin-bow of sound arched over the wide confines of the fantastic city, and suddenly there is everywhere the smell of food where before the air held only the dry tang of spice. The voices of the beggars are silent; the predominant sound now is of dancers' drums. Turbaned figures eating bowls of thick *harrissa* soup sit huddled on my doorstep, for it is the only free seat above ground-level. The light goes altogether, and I linger on because I have become one of the alley's ghosts.

One night I woke from a dream to hear the blind beggar's invocation from the street outside mingled with my own voice saying: 'Give me back my eyes.' But to whomever these words were addressed they were no more heeded than the beggar's, who asked so little while I asked so much. At dawn I would wake, or half-wake, from the tension of my dreams; I remember, objectively, that I would slip my feet out of bed and remain sitting there for long, with my eyes resting unfocused upon some ancient obscene scrawl or upon some crevice in the crumbling plaster of my cell. An Arab friend said to me: 'You must go – otherwise you never will. People can die like this, without reason; they turn inward and they are against themselves.'

Again, I dream that I am following the footprints of somebody who is lost. They are plain at first, for I walk in the red dust of a desert, and I pass the bones of a camel. Somewhere close at hand there is a palm oasis, but I skirt it as though by intention. Presently the sky seems to become lower above my head; I realise that I have left the desert and begun to climb. I am in the dry bed of a river filled with shale and stones, and at my flanks are low brick-coloured cliffs of dry earth. (Curious stones are embedded in this bank, like raisins in a cake.) The footprints have become very difficult to follow, and all the time the sky is getting lower and darker. Then I see where someone has scrambled up the mud wall at one side of the river. I try to struggle up, but the loose grit gives beneath my fingers and my feet, and my mouth is choked with dust so that I gasp for breath. I seem always to be slipping further and further downward, but I never regain the river bed

I have left. A hand that I can feel but cannot see grips my right wrist and pulls me upward with enormous strength. It relinquishes me upon the lip of the drop, and I lie there with the feeling of the thick red dust packed under my finger-nails. My throat is dry and hurts terribly, but I am filled with a feeling of urgency, and I rise and begin to climb again. I am sure of the trail, and yet I cannot see it, for I am climbing through harsh knee-high aromatic shrubs that rasp against my clothing, and it is almost dusk. Then I understand that I am following a blood trail; even in the dimness the drops glow like rubies on the small hard leaves. The slope becomes always steeper and steeper; it rises to meet the sky, and then suddenly I am beyond the line of verdure and out on the clean mountain snow. Now the footprints are clear once more, but there is blood in the centre of each. I am labouring and far gone in exhaustion, and to make sure of following the trail I place my own naked feet in the naked prints before me. Then the sky closes in upon me and I stop, for I know that the trail I am following is my own.

> All through the night I watched the ruined door,
> Intent, as gamblers watch the fall of dice;
> Awaiting verdict, prisoner at the bar.
> Shadows crossed it, once I heard a voice.
>
> At dawn a mountain hind emerged alone,
> Quick step and sure as with some purpose known,
> Some will that animates the unmarrowed bone,
> For through her ribs I saw the lichened stone.
>
> At noon a naked form was there;
> A watcher, indistinct, began
> To follow as it turned and ran
> Seaward over the shore.
>
> At dusk a broken wheel appeared
> Held by a hand I could not see,
> And I knew that someone whom I feared
> Had discovered an empty room in me.

His Excellency Moulay Ahmed El Alaoui, scion of the ruling royal Alaouite dynasty of Morocco, cousin of the Sultan who had returned from exile as His Majesty King Mohammed V, and intimate of the heir apparent, Moulay Hassan, combined, at that time the multiple appointments of Minister of Information, Minister of Tourism, and Minister of Fine Arts; in one of these roles I have already mentioned his activities at Agadir. We had for some time been acquaintances, but each awaited, I think, a nearer intellectual contact than was forthcoming on either side. We shared, I now perceive, common and paradoxical qualities of extreme shyness and extreme arrogance, drawing from each of us a sidelong glance of mutual recognition.

Moulay Ahmed, like many less exalted Moors brought up under the colonial regime of France, had suffered from eye disease and was blind in one eye; the other was roving, observant, mistrustful and xenophobe, but essentially *sympathique*. My habit of wearing dark glasses, due to chronic conjunctivitis following a dust storm in the desert two years before, had excited his adverse criticism, though it was not without precedent at court. (Mohammed V had virtually started a fashion that French 'councillors' were quick to seize upon as an example of ill manners.) This, together with a typically British reluctance to commit myself to foreign languages, had earned me from Moulay Ahmed the name of *Gavin le taciturne*, a noteworthy example of elevation from the timid to the sinister. At one time and another I had called Moulay Ahmed by many different and not always complimentary names, according to the mercurial flow of his temperament and its effects, adverse or otherwise, upon my own activities.

In late February 1961, Moulay Ahmed had for some time been intermittently preoccupied with the impending visit of two British notables whose true status had remained an enigma to me. According to Moulay Ahmed, their names were Monsieur Blanchehead and the Duc de Blitz, and they were two *grands chasseurs* for whom he was issuing special permits to shoot moufflon (the great wild Barbary sheep of Morocco) in the Atlas Mountains. In vain I protested that among the British ducal

houses there was no such alarming title as the Duke of Blitz, apt
though it might appear for a famous big-game hunter, and that
Blanchehead was at the least an improbable English name. This
last misnomer resolved itself into 'Kenneth Whitehead', a name
as then unfamiliar to me, but on the authenticity of His Grace of
Blitz Moulay Ahmed remained unshakeable. These two were to
arrive at Casablanca on the 26th, and as honoured guests of the
government, Moulay Ahmed deemed it fitting that he should
meet them in person.

Now despite the eminence of his several offices Moulay Ahmed
possessed no car, and on more than one previous occasion he had
availed himself of my own Sahara Land Rover, whose many
modifications made it a moderately dignified and not uncom-
fortable form of transport. (In fact he was so charmed by this car
that he had considered, for at least fifteen seconds, ordering an
exactly similar one for his own use.) It was therefore no great
surprise to me when he suggested that I should drive him to
Casablanca from Rabat to meet Mr Whitehead and the mysteriously explosive nobleman. He wished to leave Rabat at six
o'clock in the morning, and urged me to be waiting him
punctually at that time. This arrangement was made two days
before the arrival of the British party. I did not expect to see
Moulay Ahmed in the intervening period, more especially as I
knew that the following day the king was to undergo some minor
operation and that this would inevitably throw the whole palace
government into a state of confusion.

On the afternoon in question I had just finished lunch and was
drinking a cup of coffee on the terrace of the Tour Hassan Hotel
when a page brought me a message that His Excellency the
Minister of Information was in a car below and wished to speak to
me at once. It did not occur to me that I should be away for more
than a minute or two, so I left my coffee unfinished and my
cigarette burning in the ashtray. Outside I found Moulay Ahmed
in a handsome car driven by a resident Frenchman whom I knew
slightly, an amateur of Berber folklore; his photographs and tape
recordings were well known in modern Moroccan cultural
circles. Moulay Ahmed beckoned me to the back seat. '*Monte*,

mon cher,' he said, 'we are going for a little drive.' I excused myself on the grounds of an engagement in a quarter of an hour, but he would take no refusal. '*Monte, mon cher*,' he repeated, 'we shall be back in ten minutes, and you can keep your appointment.' There seemed no answer to this, so I got in. 'But where are we going?' I asked. 'Just for a little drive – it's such a beautiful day – just for ten minutes.' We left the town, and went northwards along the cliff-line; soon we had left the roads and tracks altogether and we were driving on smooth, hard, green pasture. I had never seen Moulay Ahmed in this mood before; he picked flowers and rhapsodised over their beauty, exulted in the smell of fennel crushed in his hand, and explained to me exactly how it should be used in cooking fish. He was like a child on a holiday in the country, finding delight in all around him. By the time I was half an hour late for my appointment I decided that it was best forgotten.

Some two hours after we had set out Moulay Ahmed looked at his watch, and gave a sudden exclamation. 'Quick! I must be at the airport at four o'clock to meet the king's surgeon from Switzerland, and we have only just enough time. Drive straight to that road over there.' He indicated a row of houses some half a mile or more away, where a single parked car suggested the presence of at least a track connecting with civilisation.

When we reached the road we were separated from it by a ditch some six feet wide and six feet deep. There was no bridge. The owner of the little parked car had emerged from his house and was preparing to drive away. Yelling at this unfortunate to stop in the name of the government, Moulay Ahmed jumped out, cleared the ditch with a flying leap, and in a matter of seconds was under way in his commandeered transport. His voice came back on the wind: 'Follow me to the airport.'

'That's all very well,' remarked the Frenchman, with the faintest ruffling of his normally suave demeanour, 'but exactly how are we supposed to follow him to the airport, *hein*?'

We cruised up the ditch and down the ditch, but there was no way across it. Finally, we had to return the way we had come, and take the conventional route from the town to the airport.

There everything was in confusion. The reception committee was vast, and at its heart was Moulay Ahmed, talking vehemently. Some said the surgeon had lost his instruments en route (I never learned whether there was any truth in this widely circulated rumour). At the end of half an hour or so there was a general movement towards the cars, and I seized a fleeting opportunity to pluck at the harassed Moulay Ahmed's sleeve. 'You won't need us any more now?' His single sound eye looked at me distractedly and irritably. 'Yes, yes, follow in the procession to the hotel.'

Once arrived there it was even more difficult to secure his much-divided attention, but I was determined that there should be no further misunderstanding. I had the audacity to stand between him and the door so that he could not enter without somehow clarifying the situation. I said: 'Is that all now, until six o'clock in the morning?' 'Yes, you may go now – but please be punctual in the morning, six o'clock here without fail.'

I got up at a quarter past five, and I was waiting in the car at six. I was still waiting in the car at eight. By then I thought I might as well breakfast in the hotel. I did so, and then telephoned to Moulay Ahmed's private number, but there was no reply. The hotel informed me that they had called him by telephone at five a.m. – it was his habit, since he lived in a small flat without servants, to have himself awoken every morning in this manner so out of keeping with his status. I tried him at the Ministry, for, being of largely nocturnal habit, there was no hour in the twenty-four at which he might not sometimes be found there (many a distant *caid* or *khalifa* had reason to resent this idiosyncracy, finding himself dragged from a deep provincial sleep at three a.m. to answer by telephone how many Danish tourists had visited his area in 1959, or the exact species of fish available to sportsmen in some remote lake of the Atlas Mountains), but the Ministry was closed. I telephoned to both numbers every half hour throughout the morning, and by one o'clock I was beginning to become fretful. At half-past one I explained the situation to a government official of my acquaintance, but not of my approval, who had sauntered into the hotel. 'No doubt he has his reasons,' he replied, eyeing me with detestation. And I had mine, I said, and began to expatiate on the theme that if the Minister of Tourism wanted help from a foreigner it would be fitting to display more courtesy. He looked at me with profound malevolence. 'If you don't like this country, why don't you get out of it and stay out?' That, I replied, was precisely what I intended to do. It was not a happy encounter.

I remained in the hotel until four o'clock in the afternoon, when this same official brought me a message from Moulay Ahmed. He was unable to go to Casablanca; would I therefore go there at once myself and find the Duke of Blitz's party at such and such a hotel. There I would please take charge. 'And do what?' I asked. 'That's all he said.'

I was going south anyway, so I would, I thought, call at the hotel and explain to the unfortunate duke what had happened. I arrived in Casablanca at half past five.

The Duke and Duchess of Blitz were more intelligible as Mr and Mrs Ian Biggs; with them was Mr Kenneth Whitehead and a young French *pied noir* who kept an inn in the mountains. On Moulay Ahmed's instructions he had driven two hundred miles to meet the party; he was to arrange their hunting trip, but Moulay Ahmed had issued no permits, and like myself this unfortunate had received no further instruction of any sort; he had expected to be briefed by Moulay Ahmed in Casablanca. We sat in a circle, glumly discussing what to do. Eventually we reached the conclusion that it would be better for the party to spend the night in the hotel and telephone to the Ministry in the morning. We were half-way through dinner, when I became aware of a curious sound in the street outside. It was unmistakably wailing, and it grew in volume every second.

Mrs Biggs went out into the hall and asked one of the hotel staff what had happened. He looked terrified, and stammered as he replied. 'They say the king is dead.'

The implications of this news took little time to sink in; to anyone having even the smallest knowledge of Morocco the situation was grave in the extreme. The heir, now King Hassan II, was not, at that time, popular in the country; there were strong undercurrents of political and personal feelings; more than one party aspired to seize power, and Morocco has never enjoyed a reputation for pacific persuasion. In fact, a revolution appeared, at the least, very probable. One thing, anyway, seemed obvious – this put paid to the Duke of Blitz's hunting trip, and would probably have done so even if the Ministries of Tourism and of Information had not been combined. Morocco would become a nation in mourning for its first hero of independence; a nation in fear, too, and probably under military rule; there would be no time for frivolities such as big-game hunting. The Frenchman, André Deschaseaux (who later became a close friend of mine), would know all this much better than I, but I was doubtful of our capacity to convey it to the single-minded Blitz party. André, being a Frenchman among four Englishmen, left it to me, and I was not wholly successful. I tried to explain by stages; the fact, the political implications, finally the probable effect upon the personal plans of any foreign visitor. One could not blame them for taking it hardly; they had planned this journey – not, incidentally, an inexpensive one – a long time before; they had received assurances and promises, and now the whole card-castle was falling to the ground. But as the sounds from the street grew more and more violent, these considerations began to appear to me increasingly minor.

When there is trouble in Morocco its centre has usually been, during this century, in Casablanca; here (and among Berber tribesmen who have often been ill-informed as to the issues involved) is the heart of violence. It seemed to me eminently desirable that the Blitz party should leave Casablanca for the south, where in many districts of the mountains a Europophile attitude still existed among the Berber tribespeople. I put forward this suggestion; that the whole party should leave now for Asni, André's inn in the foothills of the Atlas. André agreed; he anyway, he said, must return there at once, for his young wife and child were all alone. The party could be divided between the two cars, and we could travel in convoy.

But both André and myself were unknown to the visitors, and they were understandably anxious to consult higher authority before committing themselves to any immediate plan of action. The duchess telephoned to the British Embassy in Rabat, and received unequivocal counsel. There had been serious rioting in Rabat, rumours of even greater violence in certain districts of Casablanca, and the British party were strongly advised not to leave the hotel until the Embassy considered the situation restored to normal. This official recommendation they accepted; no doubt my description of my car as a Land Rover did little to convey a picture of the heavy closed vehicle it was, and was not reassuring. The ducal party decided to remain in Casablanca; André and I decided to leave for the south in convoy. Frankly, I did not expect to see the Blitzes again.

André, knowing the by-ways of the town intimately, preceded me. In some sense our survival value was divided, for while he had all the local knowledge, and was fluent both in Berber and Arabic, my car had all the appearance of officialdom, and carried the word 'Britannia' in Arab characters fore and aft and on both sides. It would also be an extremely difficult car to overturn. We had arranged that should André run into trouble he should abandon his own car and board the Land Rover.

The psychological climate of the populace seemed to vary between one quarter of the town and another. Everywhere the streets were packed; it seemed that of Casablanca's million inhabitants no human being was indoors that night. They formed a densely pressed throng right across the streets, chanting in unison, swaying, a potentially murderous mass, but as yet insufficiently organised for concerted violence. Nearer to the suburbs there were a few broken shop windows, a few overturned cars, but we were never seriously molested. A few stones, or lighter missiles, struck the body and wheels of the Land Rover, but despite the extreme scarcity of wheeled traffic on the streets there was no real attempt to arrest our snail's pace progress. The crowds gave way reluctantly to André's headlamps and horn, and immediately closed in again behind him, so that to avoid isolation I had to keep my front bumpers within inches of his rear.

Once clear of the town and out upon the deserted country

roads a new alarm seized me. I had noted André's extreme exhaustion, and now, following him at the prearranged speed of 110 k.p.h. that was the Land Rover's maximum, I was horrified to see that every few minutes he would give a wild swerve that took the car to within centimetres of the road's edge. I imagined that on each of these occasions he had momentarily fallen asleep; and it was with enormous effort that I overtook him and persuaded him to stop. I explained my fears. He grinned. 'Don't worry; when I am very tired, very sleepy, this is my way of keeping myself awake; I should have told you. As long as I do that I never fall asleep.'

The first of the road-blocks was out by the time we reached Settat; there had been serious rioting and many dead, but the army were now in control. We reached Marrakesh at one thirty, and there André and I parted company, he to Asni, and I to the single room I rented in the *medina*.

Morocco during the following week was ominous; the explosion seemed imminent. I awoke early in the morning to the sound of children's voices chanting in a short, staccato, uncompromising rhythm. From my window I could see the procession marching down the street in step to the words of their chant: '*Bas, bas Moulay Hassan! Bas, bas Moulay Hassan!*' (down with Moulay Hassan). One glance at the demonstrators showed that this was an organised programme; there were perhaps two hundred of them, and they were all of the same age group, say between eight and twelve years old. They passed on their way, and all was quiet again, the streets deserted.

An hour later the sound of the same refrain came near, but this time the voices were tenor rather than treble, for this was a different group, some five hundred boys of between twelve and fifteen years. After a further hour came an older group of adolescents; then at about mid-morning came a thousand men marching to the same hymn of hate, '*Bas, bas Moulay Hassan!*' It was clear that whether or not there was to be a revolution there was at least going to be a bull-frog show of strength on both sides. I went down to the *Gueliz*, which before independence used to be the French town, to glean what news I could. The central Post Office, an enormous building, presented the most extraordinary spectacle. It was shut, and guarded by something like a battalion of soldiery with fixed bayonets. In front of this closed rank patrolled numerous officers armed with submachine-guns. Nearer, the whole square was a dense mass of Moroccan humanity. They moved slowly, viscously, unnaturally silent; only occasionally, from the heart of the crowd, a single voice, certain of anonymity, called out the words of rebellion, '*Bas Moulay Hassan!*'

Mingling innocently with this menacing press were a few wide-eyed American tourists in the charge of city guides. There are some thirty of these guides in Marrakesh; of these only two, I think, speak any English. One of them is semi-attached to the Mamounia Hotel, and now I overheard fragments of conversation between his clients and himself.

'Say, Abdullah, what are these guys calling out – something about Hassan?'

'They are saying "Long live our new Sultan".'

'And what are the soldiers doing?'

'They parade in honour of our new Sultan.'

'Well, that's swell, but I guess I got to get to that Post Office somehow – I got mail to collect.'

'The Post Office is closed; it is a day of national holiday in honour of the new Sultan.'

'Does this holiday last more than one day?'

'It is not yet known,' the guide answered with aplomb and good humour. 'It may last for some time.'

It did, in fact, last for some time. During it, certain curious documents in my possession came into their own. Some weeks before Moulay Ahmed had, with a characteristically impulsive generosity, furnished me with certain papers whose utility I had not at the time fully appreciated or foreseen. The first of these was a page-long letter in Arabic characters that I am unable to read: it has been so variously translated to me that it is difficult to choose a rendering. (My mule boy in the mountains pored over it for several minutes, nodding contentedly to himself; when at length he handed it back to me, I asked him what it meant. '*De ne pas vous frapper*,' he summed up succinctly.) The second item, of infinitely greater power in emergency, was a police *coupe file*, a thick rectangle of pasteboard twice the size of a visiting card, and bearing across it a diagonal strip of the red and green police colours. Such cards are no rarity in themselves; they are not infrequently issued to the press for strictly limited periods varying from a half an hour to a day. Mine, however, was permanent and without date, and it allowed me to contravene any police regulation or order. Whether in fact it would have excused a murder I never put to the test, but certainly it dealt with every imaginable kind of traffic offence, swept me past police or army road-blocks and, used in conjunction with the letter ordering people not to strike me, bore me merrily through customs and customs police formalities.

In return for such capricious favours bestowed by Moulay Ahmed I had collaborated with him in various egregious projects. The most ignominious of these, as I remember it, was the dubbing with English commentary of a Moroccan documentary film on the first pan-African conference at Casablanca. The film, at the time when I attempted the dubbing, had been joined in random sequence and without cutting; it was only shown during my recording, it was explained to me, in order to clarify the time factor. The result was chaos. At first the screen showed the bows of a large but antiquated yacht cutting through a calm sea. 'Now for the first time,' I began sonorously (I had put much con-scientious work into this, and was determined to give value for favours received), 'the white bows of the yacht *Harriyah*, whose name means freedom, carve the calm waters of Casablanca harbour. With renewed hope for the future of Africa' (cut to a long shot of a West African potentate whose dignified white robes are blown above the waist by an airfield hurricane; frenzied attendants try to restore him to decency). I stammer, and con-tinue a little wildly: 'We are here to welcome President Nasser himself, who salutes the flag of Moroccan independence as on this historic occasion he stands upon *Harriyah*'s deck seeing our shores for the first time. . . .' (cut to a close-up of a small fishing boat trying frantically to avoid the *Harriyah*). I choke, but manage to continue with some hesitation: 'At this solemn moment when the eyes of all the world are upon us . . .' (suddenly the screen is filled with a hilarious banqueting scene – zoom in to the preternaturally gigantic face of Nkrumah; the film suddenly speeds up until he is eating chocolates and roaring with silent laughter in a mad, hysteric frenzy), 'when, ahem, the eyes of all the world are upon us . . .' (flickers, flashes, a clapperboard with the legend Take One, then the bows of *Harriyah*, but this time going backwards, followed by Nkrumah spewing out whole chocolates into his hand.) 'For Chrisake,' I said, '*no one* could dub this film' – but I was there for a further hour.

Now with the country in a state of national emergency my papers were more than a luxury toy, they were a *sine qua non*. But for the moment I had forgotten them.

When, some hours later, I tried to return to the *medina* I encountered a road-block at its periphery. Two machine-guns were very much in evidence. An officer carrying a submachine-gun approached my window; I observed with disapproval that this weapon was cocked and that the safety catch was off. 'Where are you going?' he asked. 'To the *medina*.' 'The *medina* is closed – no car may enter or leave.' 'But,' I protested, 'I live there, and I need the car.' 'It is impossible, turn round and go back.' Suddenly I remembered my talismans, and produced from my wallet the letter and the *coupe file*. He glanced quickly at them; then, 'You should have shown me these at once,' he said, and at a rapid order the road-block was opened.

There was an armed sentry at my door. 'Why are you here?' I asked. 'My orders,' he said briefly. I could not tempt him into conversation.

All the afternoon following the death of the king the sound of lamentation came from somewhere behind the mosque of the Koutabia, a chant whose very simplicity and constant repetition evoked some unfathomable ocean of grief. '*Ya Sidna! Ya Sidna! Ya Sidna!*' (Oh our Lord), the note of the middle syllable held for long seconds before falling with a sob to the last.

One evening at the close of Ramadan . . .

After what was, in the circumstances, a surprisingly short delay, the Duke of Blitz's hunting trip was arranged. I accompanied them on the second day. On mule-back we climbed long ridges of the foothills among pungent shrubs and flowering lavender; the rifles took up their positions looking out across a gorge while some fifty Berber beaters swept a few miles of country towards them. Each of us shot a wild boar, and in response to excited urgings from my Berber companion I contributed an unfortunate three-legged jackal.

On the first day the party had set out to shoot moufflon, but I was feeling too ill to accompany them. One moufflon was killed (these giant wild sheep have become rare in Morocco since the massive depredations of the Army of Liberation while living off the country), and the next morning the two Moroccan daily newspapers carried front-page pictures of a moufflon draped over my Land Rover. 'In the presence of the famous English writer, Gavin Maxwell, two superb moufflons weighing respectively . . . and . . . were shot by the noted English sportsmen Mr Biggs and Mr Whitehead.' I was sorry to see the duke thus summarily demoted at his hour of triumph but impressed by the size of the moufflons, which to my certain knowledge had never been weighed.

I had a friend who announced for the English-speaking pro-gramme of a North African radio station. Part of her weekly routine was to read the 'Answers to your Questions'; questions that ranged from space travel to pantheism, from spelaeology to politics. The replies that she read were, in fact, those sent in by anonymous experts often from distant countries, but she felt that her public might find irksome the double anonymity of their advisers and her voice. For me, therefore, she conceived the role of a master mind present in the studio, a mysterious Professor

Svenski, who knew the answers to all these questions without previous consultation, a miraculous combination of Bronowski, Russell, Huxley, and all the great specialised scientists of the decade. Affecting a stateless middle-European accent perfected by much imitative practice during the war years, I played my part in this mischievous comedy for two successive weeks; a third time, we thought, would tempt exposure, and it was announced that Professor Svenski had left the country for Indonesia.

Thus it was my friend and not I who, the following week, answered a question concerning flying saucers, and to my infinite regret it was she rather than Professor Svenski who received the letter in reply:

'Darling,

'Yesterday when I was listening to the American emission of radio I heard you proclaim with royal assurance that flying saucers existed only in people's imagination though many times photographs of the "flying objects" as you call them officially have been published. Up to now I don't suppose that anybody has discovered that cameras had imagination. If so an official report of the fact should have been made to all academies of science. As a fact, flying saucers do exist and it is a happy thing that they do, because the pilots of these flying machines are former inhabitants of this earth, or at least many of them. They are what the hebrews call angels and what the greeks called the ferry men of the Styx. After your death they will take you on a non-stop flight to another planet, where you will lead your heavenly life. In 1949 began an angel display organised by God to prove once more to modern man who no longer believes in his existence that he is still in life. . . . Today a whole planet is wrapped in idolatry and the celebration of a false God called Jesus Christ whilst the true God to whom public appraise should be given is left in the dark. As a fact, you can speak of him to anyone in the street using his proper name Iaveh and no one will understand you.

'It is he who bygone religions called the Sun God, or more exactly the Shining Monarch, because he irradiates light all about his person.

74

'The prophet Ezekiel gives a description of him when he saw him for the first time on a flying saucer. Some time ago he appeared in Morocco and Moroccans speak of this apparation as "The Sultan of the Moon".* You can ask your surroundings to check this statement.

'Another fact is that a flying saucer really landed in America, and the pilot of the machine spoke to a polishman called Adamski, now living in America and the visitor gave explanations to Mr Adamski who did not realise the real meaning of it.

1. He told Mr Adamski that he lived a long time ago on this planet but that now he lived on the planet Venus. As men die, Mr Adamski was in the presence of what we call a resurrected man.

2. Mr Adamski believed in the resurrection of man after death. He is a theosopher it seems but so much foolish ideas have been spread with spiritism about ectoplasmas, etc., that the visitor showed Mr Adamski that his astral body as theosophists call it was made of real matter that you could weigh on a balance and he walked on the ground weighing on his feet and pointed to the depth of his footprints. Mr Adamski did not take the hint, but he made mouldings of the footprints and still wonders at their meaning.

'Of course conversation was difficult because the two persons did not speak the same language, but the acts recorded by Mr Adamski have meanings. Three friends of Mr Adamski witnessed his interview and signed sworn certificates that it was true, so nobody has the right to consider him a liar. One of the witnesses even made a drawing of the man Mr Adamski saw. Who is he?

'The information I have about the saucers was given to me by God himself. I have written it in a book of which 26 volumes were sent to the United Nations in New York to be distributed to leading chiefs of state. Up to now I have never received any answer, and I don't know what they became.

'Anyhow, when God spoke to me for the first time . . . he told me that his name was Iaveh, and that I would remember it because

* A reference to the fact that after the exile in 1954 of Sultan Mohammed V of Morocco, many Moors claimed to discern his profile in the surface contours of the full moon. (Author.)

it resembled my own name; I just had to change the first syllable of my name. If the same thing was done with Mr Adamski you can have Adam-ski, in which case it is probable that Mr Adamski had the honour of speaking to nobody else but *Adam* himself, and looking at the drawing made of him scientists may contemplate the monkey who is responsible of our lives.

'Facts are facts, and if official scientists are pleased at acting like fools we can't help it; as things are there are two messengers of God actually on earth: Mr Adamski and myself. If Mr Adamski enraptured by all the wonders he saw has gone astray in a poetical view of space and creation I am all right in every detail, but nobody wants to listen to me or publish what I write on the subject.

'As for cobwebs, I see many of them but only in the minds of people who deny the existence of saucers.

'After reading my book that I am sending you I hope that you will be convinced, and if afterwards you manage to convince the American nation you will then be a great girl and all America will be at your feet. With regards to me, it is now 15 years that I am trying to interest somebody to the facts revealed to me by God without success. . . . Hoping that you will find pleasure in discovering that fairies do exist and that the King of the fairies is God himself and a great magician, I remain. . . .'

The book accompanying this letter was a cyclostyled manuscript of something like a hundred thousand words, devoted in part to reasoned and clear-thinking destruction of the organised religions of the world – here the author's rapier-thrusts were skilful and deadly – and in part to a rich madness of fantasy, in which God zoomed about through time and space on flying saucers and flying cigars. The book was entitled *God's Orders for all Kings the World Over*, and it opened with a declaration.

I hereby solemnly declare that God . . . appeared to me when I was a child . . . and gave me explanations which he wanted to be brought to the knowledge of the Pope and to all leaders of nations the world over. . . . In December 1939 . . . God again appeared to me and reminded me of our meeting. He gave me mission to write his explanations and give them to French authorities. In 1944, with much pains, I managed to get about all together and wrote a document on the subject that I sent to General de Gaulle then in Algiers. . . . He never answered my letter.

Nobody wished to see into the matter and it is now eleven years that I am looking for a comprehensive mind. . . . Effectively I am the Anti-Christ of Christian prophecy, and my mission is to declare to the face of the world that Christians worship in Jesus Christ a false God. . . .

Maybe, I thought, as I read on through the ten long chapters, but his own deity appeared almost wholly preoccupied by aeronautics.

In ancient days when God went about the world building empires he travelled in a flying machine that we call today a flying cigar . . . the spirits who accompanied him were called angels and travelled in flying saucers. . . . As a fact, God supervised the hebrews' flight from Egypt on a flying cigar. . . . In later years Ezekiel sees him again in his flying cigar accompanied by saucers . . . and four other flying machines which he calls 'cherubins' which seem to be aerostatic machines. . . . As God explained to me, the Statue of Mercury, messenger of the Gods, represents an angel . . . the hat that the sculptor put on the head of his angel is not a hat but the saucer in which he flied. . . . As a fact, a few years ago, God flew over Washington and the States escorted by saucers, unrecognised and unsaluted. . . . I was a child of seven years old when I had the honour of seeing God the Father.

(They got on very well together, and God entrusted to the author the task of explaining to the Pope his mistakes.) Exodus 'tells . . . how the Jews crossed the Red Sea, God leading them always by day and by night in a flying cigar. . . . The following morning God looked out from his cigar on the Egyptian camp and put

77

disorder among them. . . .' (At some points, however, he appears cautious, not to say timorous, for having skilfully landed his flying cigar on Mount Sinai, he gave Moses instructions to keep his people at a distance 'because he feared a rush'. But 'he did no harm to them and gave them refreshments'.)

This extraordinary document, a racy reinterpretation of the Bible followed by an appraisal and critique of the major religions of the world, lacking neither inspiration nor intelligence (except when its author rode a hobby horse or a flying saucer) ended with letters to the heads of all states giving God's instructions. They were nothing if not precise. The general letter prefacing those to individuals gives God's basic requirements for successful administration:

> In the temple, there must be a private room furnished like the office of a modern business man at God's disposition where he can write his instructions for the king if he has any to give. [A ruler must] await God's appearance with his officials and ask him his instructions . . . if God is sulking and does not appear then he must order burnt sacrifices as they were accomplished in the past. . . . If God wishes to come he can do so as he did in ancient days in a saucer and land on an aerodrome but we cannot oblige him in this case.

To the Pope:

> *Vous êtes prié, en tant que chef de L'Eglise du Christ, de convoquer un concile au plus tôt et faire reconnaitre par celui-ci que le Christian-isme est une heresie et mettre fin ensuite a l'activité de L'Eglise. . . . En terminant, je vous prie d'agréer, Signor, l'expression de mes condoléances pour vos idées perdues.*

To the Queen of England:

> Graceful Queen, . . . with regard to the Christian faith, every-thing in it is false and it is God's will that you put an end to it all over your empire. He appears as a distinguished gentleman and has no wish to harm a distinguished lady like you. . . . I

78

beg you on my knees to believe in me and accordingly show the nations on earth that you are a great girl. . . . Through . . . a german alliance a drop of this blood that runs in my veins runs also in yours. This is too far off for me to call you my dear cousin but it means that I have no interest in trifling with your feelings, on the contrary.

The longest and most peremptory epistle was reserved for the President of the French Republic; it ran to several thousand words, and ended: '*En vous rappelant que je vous remets, ce jour, de la part de Dieu, un ordre au sens militaire du mot, je vous prie de'agréer.* . . .'

Inside the folder cover of this mighty manuscript was affixed a printed label *Please accuse reception.* I am afraid we never did accuse it, any more than did United Nations or the heads of states.

Darkness on the waterfront in Algiers; a scuffle and a high bubbling cry. A burst of submachine-gun fire close at hand and a window splinters somewhere overhead. I turn the corner; no one has moved him. He lies there, an elderly Arab with beard jutting to the sky. There is more blood than I would have believed possible; I had not seen a slit throat before. A group of French parachutists swagger by; one kicks the corpse. Curfew, and an ill-hidden microphone in my bedroom.

Morning, and the city under lashing rain; all along the water-front the high waves rolled in, not Mediterranean blue nor nordic grey, but mud brown with dark Algerian sand, and when the crests curled over and the spume streamed back on the wind it too was brown. A French bar-tender looked out on it and said: 'It is an omen – the brown tide, the Arab tide that will sweep us all away, and unlike this tide it will not recede.' I ordered cognac; he poured two and raised his glass, 'Algérie Française'. He looked to me to respond; I raised my glass vaguely and said, 'Algérie!' What other answer could there be?

One night I wandered on a salt-marsh; I left the streets of the city in which I was living because without solitude I could not resolve the tangle of my thoughts. When I set out the moon was bright;

I walked upon turf causeways imposed rectilinearly upon pans of flooded land stretching endlessly to the edge of a river delta. Before me rose ghostly flocks of flamingoes; they wheeled pale but colourless in the moonlight, and alighted always ahead of me, so that their numbers became illimitable and all-enveloping. After a long time the moon was hidden by cloud and I could no longer follow their flight. The only possible paths were the now unlit causeways, running always at right angles to each other, and I had lost my bearings. In utter darkness I came upon a *bidonville* shack. A figure little darker than the sky was somehow beside me and drew me into the warm darkness of the shelter. A bellows fanned a charcoal brazier, a bearded face thus lit by firelight glanced at me without apparent curiosity. '*Min fdl'k,*' he said. '*Min fdl'k*' (make yourself at home), and leaving the brazier he spread a blanket on the floor. I drank mint tea and then slept; in the cold hour of the dawn I was aware that small children came and laid more coverings upon me. No one asked me any questions.

Two hundred miles away from the beggars and my *garçonnière* is the other room round which my life centred during the haywire winter. The number of times that I have traversed that route seems now uncountable, though a precise analysis would no doubt be disappointing. It is enough, anyway, to know every curve, every undulation. As with any long road that a traveller follows often, it has stretches that seem inimical and others that are reassuring. Physically, it is virtually without incident, the vast plain is given life only by small human activity and by changing sheets of flowers. Early in the year I would watch the harnessed camels ploughing the red earth, followed by a snowy froth of cattle egrets, as gulls follow the plough in Europe. There were league-long carpets of big white daisies where no green showed between them, and low hills between whose scrub were unbroken acres of mingled orange and purple flowers, painted, one would say, by a pointilliste such as Seurat. Other images of the road: high wind and tossing avenues of eucalyptus trees showing the white undersides to their leaves, eddies of red dust racing in high spirals along their ranks; biblical shepherds in tattered robes watching over piebald sheep who at the edge of green and unprotected corn graze conscientiously upon nothing; slow processions of camels laden with dates or halfa grass; bobbing, tittupping rows of donkeys whose white-turbaned riders sit side-saddle far back upon the crupper; a small mêlée in mid-road which, as the car surges down upon it, resolves itself into two tiny children trying to wrest the tail from a squashed jackal; the wreckage of a giant Cadillac wrapped round the stem of a eucalyptus tree, a bloodless corpse in a white *djellabah* hanging through the glassless window.

This road, after several hours of fierce driving, leads to the home of Prudence Hazell. Her wide window, fringed by a collection of cactuses that seem to have nothing at all to do with her personality, looks out over an orderly modern square in a town of progress. Here the men wear European clothes; the women, however, remain veiled, anonymous, and Prudence's maid, Aysha, becomes a totally unrecognisable figure of mystery as soon as she steps outside the door.

Everything else but the cactuses reflects some aspect of Prudence's personality. The sparse furniture, of which the *pièce de résistance* is formed by two twelve-foot-long mattresses, one against each wall; the bright North African blankets and cushions that cover them; the elaborate wall-hangings from Far Eastern civilisations; the great debris of papers and books, that occasionally starts within itself a landslide and spreads contemporary events over the floor like rock-fall on a mountain road; the telephone with its apparently inexhaustible length of flex; the overworked typewriter whose style has become staccato owing to the death of its minor punctuation marks – all these things belong as unmistakably to Prudence as does a thorn bush larder to a desert shrike. Contrary to impression, every book and document in the paper-storm of her table is securely impaled upon some mental thorn; she holds them under the calm surveillance of her glass-grey eyes as she holds friends, enemies, and acquaintances of many nationalities. Impaled too, upon the million spines whose zareba forms the periphery of her consciousness, is every fact that she has ever read or learned, every face and name that she has ever known; for though Prudence in middle age has travelled and read more widely than do most men in a lifetime, she has a memory whose precision retains the minute detail of every experience, whether firsthand or vicarious.

While by no means lacking in the domestic virtues she is pleased on occasion to allow her guests a display of their dexterity. At this moment that I picture her she sits at a table in the corner of the room, alternatively sucking a red pencil and deleting with it portions of a typewritten document; on one of the long mattress sofas the Utopian Ambassador, as black as night, is repairing one of her gloves whose finger-seam has split; at the opposite end squats the Chief of the Balongan Trade Delegation, sewing a button on to her jacket sleeve. I am between them, trying to repair the zip-fastener of her mountaineering anorak. She looks up. 'I'm sorry to be so unsociable, my dears, but I must get this done tonight – Nkrumah is coming to lunch tomorrow, and all those Ambassadors. . . .'

The doorbell rings. Prudence steps quickly into the hall and closes behind her the frosted-glass sliding doors that separate the sitting-room from the hall. There is a long muted conversation beyond them; it may be in any one of the ten languages that Prudence speaks fluently. At the end of ten minutes she returns and resumes her interrupted work without comment. Her guests leave very late, but if it is before two o'clock in the morning they are inevitably replaced by newcomers before I can dispose myself to sleep upon one of the long mattresses. When I do so there is usually a representative of some unliberated or imperfectly liberated country snoring upon the sofa opposite. Such men live in an atmosphere into which I am drawn as inexorably as a fly into the maw of an insect-eating plant, an atmosphere of intrigue and sudden death. They are good enough to explain to me that our fortuitous association may be interpreted to my disadvantage; in Africa, they warn me, everyone is assumed to be partisan, and a British author at large is a suspect figure. They advise me to inspect my car for bombs every morning; at this, while my more habitual proficiencies flag, I have become quick and unforgetful.

My existence became shaped like a dumb-bell; at one end the orbit of my own dimly lit and squalid room, at the other the international clearing-house of Prudence Hazell's flat. Far to the south were the bright deserts where I longed to be, the deserts of shimmering castellated mirage and bounding gazelles, the flowering deserts where from waterless stone *jol* grew the miracle of mauve blossom upon pale thorn; but far to the south, too, were the columns of burning gas from the oil wells at Hassi Messaoud, pillars of smoke by day and of fire by night.

I would try sometimes to think of Camusfeàrna in March sunshine, of the waterfall and the budding birches, of primroses among dead bracken, of the soft mountain distances and blue sea, but always the image would dissolve before it was complete. before it was strong enough to draw me from where I was. Again and again I postponed my return, unable to break through the confines of a barrier I could not understand. I was aware that I needed some jolt into reality to awaken me and to bring me home, and that that jolt could only come from some part of Camusfeàrna. As a result of this slender awareness I took the first positive step towards mental self-preservation. I wrote to England saying that I had been unwell for some weeks and suggesting that Jimmy Watt be sent out to help me with my return journey. I knew that he himself would be overjoyed, for he had always wanted to travel, but I was still afraid that the sight of him, and all its associations with homely, peaceful things, would not be enough to lift the cataract from my eyes, and that I would return in the same twilight state as I was.

Aberrant mental conditions are difficult to convey other than by implication or soliloquy; prose becomes overcharged in an effort to communicate emotion that is not fully understood by the writer. That, anyway, is nearly all that I can write of the hay-wire winter. I awoke, in some sense, when I saw Jimmy's face in the queue at the passport barrier, and all that Camusfeàrna was came back to me like the breaking of a dam. As we drove in a taxi from the airport he told me of a hundred trivialities at my home, and suddenly it became the only important thing in the world.

Jimmy stayed in North Africa for a fortnight, learned to drive the Land Rover on flat desert, acquired a curious dragon-like living lizard that, among a whole witch's compendium of dried vultures' wings, hyenas' teeth, ostriches' eggs, and a hundred other unsavoury magic properties, was obscenely demonstrated by a medicine man as a cure for impotence.

Moulay Ahmed's documents still had their last and climactic function to fulfil. Our homeward passages and that of the Land Rover were booked on a Dutch cargo boat sailing from Casablanca to London, and on the previous evening we were in the Tour Hassan Hotel at Rabat. I had not seen Moulay Ahmed since the Duke of Blitz's moufflon hunt several weeks before; now, in the bar of the Tour Hassan, he requested me to attend a duck shoot in a Northern province the following week. I explained that we were leaving for England the next day. He asked how we were travelling, and I told him by cargo boat from Casablanca. 'That,' said Moulay Ahmed triumphantly, 'will not be possible. Tomorrow is the state visit to Casa of Marshal Tito, and all routes into Casa will be closed. Your route into the town would actually be the processional route. It is absolutely impossible.'
'Even with the aid of the documents you gave me?'
'Even with those. You can forget the whole idea.'
Jimmy and I conferred privately. We had, we decided, nothing to lose and everything to gain by the attempt. There was at least a chance, and the documents, together with the highly official appearance of the car formed a *combine formidable*. We did not announce our intentions to Moulay Ahmed.
We left Rabat early the next morning. The route had certainly been well prepared; every two or three miles there was an army or police road-block; and although the *coupe file* remained effective we decided upon a diversion by the minor coastal road. Upon entering Casablanca itself, however, I realised at once that Moulay Ahmed had not exaggerated, and that things were going to be very difficult indeed. Moroccan protocol for reception of heads of states is elaborate and traditional and, on such an occasion as this, included the mass importation of tribespeople from

distant districts. These line the processional route, often for miles; they carry drums and tambourins, and at the approach of the state procession they begin to drum and to sing and sway to the rhythm of archaic tribal dances.

From the extreme outskirts of Casablanca all traffic was diverted away from the broad processional route that led to the port. I did not follow this diversion; instead I drove straight up to the police point and presented my documents through the window of the car. I had not really believed their efficacy in this situation, and I was amazed when the car was waved on without question. But when I saw what lay ahead of me I came near to panic. The broad empty road stretched away for a mile or more, festive with flags and bunting, innocent of a single wheeled vehicle, but densely lined at its sides with many thousands of spectators. As we moved on, a long ripple swept forward among them; turbaned heads craned to get a view, white *djellabahs* fluttered, hands waved. There was a division of opinion as to how this lone vehicle should be treated, the first, evidently, that had passed that way all day; some, clearly, took us for outriders or heralds, and accorded us no more than a burst of clapping or a ragged cheer; the tribespeople of the hills, on the other hand, unable to interpret the Arabic lettering upon the car, and doubt-lessly unaccustomed to the format of a state procession, took us, if not for Tito himself, at least for some part of his entourage. We were clearly not Moroccans, we were driving along down the processional route, and it must have seemed reasonable to assume that we were foreign guests of honour. The adherents of this viewpoint behaved to us as they had been instructed to behave to Tito; they drummed and danced and sang and cheered, and it was a little difficult to know how to respond to this undeserved ovation. We compromised with more or less fixed smiles and an intermittent gesture between a wave and an official salute; but all the time I had a deep irrational fear that somehow Moulay Ahmed would suddenly appear like an avenging djinn from a bottle and tear our thin disguise to ignominious shreds.

But there was no disaster, no further checkpoint, the police who were in great strength nearer to the centre of the town plainly had full confidence in their colleagues at the outer defences, and eyed us almost without curiosity. The parking of the car seemed for a moment to present insuperable problems; then I reflected that no one was likely to question us further. Outside Casablanca's most luxurious hotel, which lay right on the processional route, was a car park over which was written 'Police only', and into this I drove with confidence, flashing my *coupe file* as I did so. Jimmy and I then ascended to the lofty roof of the Land Rover to watch the procession in comfort. A police officer called a question to me, and I was preparing myself for lengthy explanations when I realised that he was asking whether he might join us on the roof.

The next day we shipped the car aboard a small boat carrying a hold cargo of oranges and a deck cargo of tortoises, and lurched homeward across the Bay of Biscay below great white cumulus clouds, the blue sea and white water hissing and foaming at the ship's sides.

A year of mishaps and disasters at Camusfeàrna lay ahead, but at least I was awake and had shaken off the haywire winter. I have buried the rest of it in the compost heap of my subconscious, and now it only returns to me in the poignancy of dreams, urgent and febrile, in which are implicit the sense of some task unfinished, some goal unattained – sometimes I have thought it was death, either my own or that of the scapegoat. But only Holman Hunt could contrive the death of his goat; the others are immortal, rancid and septic, ready always to return and be driven forth again.

In completion of our ritual of sorrow
I drove you from my fold with whip and goad;
Through wildernesses where I could not follow
You bore my shed intolerable load.

Groping after you now my purpose wanders
Through dry defiles upon the world's roof;
On dimly lit Saharas of unknowledge
I trace the double imprint of your hoof.

Goat calls to goat across the distant mountain;
Your outcast taint is rank upon the air;
Your herd forms, and the lowered horns turned outward
Deny my right, long shed, to all you share.

The she-goat standing for the scapegoat's mount
Takes on her back his double load of weight –
To bear a scapekid. When we drive him out
He will come here to find a willing mate.

So in the smell of sin you will discover
That my shed load held more than guilt and pain,
And in these Ishmael herds may mate another
With love that I cannot recall again.

5

All the Wild Summer Through

With that spring following the publication of *Ring of Bright Water* the privacy of Camusfeàrna came abruptly to an end. A great number of people who read the book accepted the disguise of place names as a challenge, and were determined to locate and visit the place; they came by their hundreds, and because at first we did not wish to appear churlish the once orderly routine of the house became chaotic. As spring turned to summer and the tourist season reached its height we became desperate, for the inroads upon our time meant that I was able to work only sporadically and without concentration. We erected *Private* notices on the two tracks by which the house may be approached, but these had little effect, and gradually our days became almost wholly occupied with warding off uninvited visitors. The number of notices that these had to pass before reaching Camusfeàrna was formidable; at the distance of more than a mile all gates already carried estate notices at the entry to the forestry ground, reading *Strictly Private – Young Trees*; after a further half mile the hardy encountered the first of my own signboards – *This Is A Private Footpath To Camusfeàrna – No Unannounced Visitors Please*; then, for those who had penetrated all the outer defences, came an elaborate signboard with a drawing of a be-seeching otter and the words: *Visitors: There Are Pet Otters Here – Please Keep Dogs On Leash*; and finally, at a range of two hundred yards or so from the citadel, the single word PRIVATE, in foot-high red letters. Despite all these precautions, a steady stream of rubbernecks arrived daily, often with loose and undisciplined dogs, to bang on the single door of the house and demand, as if it were their right, to see the otters and all that had figured in the story.

One of the most extraordinary and revealing aspects of this unconcerted invasion was the conviction of each that he or she, and he or she alone, was the pioneer; that it could not have been possible for any other to have discovered the true location of Camusfeàrna, or for any other to have wished to do so. Each claimed to have established the position by hours of labour with charts and deductive power worthy of Hercule Poirot; by a long past familiarity with the coastline that had yielded a sudden and vital clue; by private information given by a friend of a friend of an acquaintance; by some recognised piece of landscape in a published photograph – always, in sum, by some feat of mental or imaginative agility of which no other could be capable. After one long day, when we had wrestled many hours with such well disguised angels, and when we were at last sitting down to eat for the first time since the previous evening, there came an authoritative rap on the door and a murmur of perceptibly trans-atlantic voices. I refused to move, and sent one of the boys to deal with the situation. The message he brought back was that the gentleman (the name eludes me) had travelled three thousand miles to see Camusfeàrna, and could not believe that I would be so inhospitable as to refuse him entry. For the first time since the beginning of the siege my temper broke; I replied that if indeed he had wished to travel three thousand miles to visit a total stranger he might have shown more courtesy than to arrive unannounced at half past nine in the evening. This churlish out-burst set a precedent, and when a few days later I looked out from my window to see a party of five people leaning over the wooden palisade and baiting (I can find no other word) Teko, I found the instinct for battle strong in me. I went out and asked them with hostile civility from where they came. Manchester, I was told. 'And in Manchester,' I asked, with what coolness my rage could master, 'is it the custom to treat your neighbour's house and garden as a public exhibit?' There was a shocked silence; then the paterfamilias said plaintively: 'But this is not

Manchester; in Scotland we've been told there's no law of trespass!'

This extraordinary situation does, in fact, obtain; in Scotland there is nothing but the unwritten rule of common civility to prevent any stranger entering the garden of a suburban or other house and making himself thoroughly at home. If he picks the flowers or otherwise damages the garden it is possible to secure an injunction against his future entry, but if he has a hundred friends lined up to repeat the performance it will be necessary to take out an injunction against each of them severally and in succession. An Englishman's home is his castle, but not a Scotsman's. Scottish law contains many such whimsical quirks; for example, a homicidal maniac may not be reincarcerated on the original findings if after escape he succeeds in remaining at liberty for three weeks. Research into the origins of such legal curiosities might be rewarding but not, one cannot help feeling, edifying.

As month succeeded month we became, in self-defence, more and more ruthless, because the very life of the place was at stake. If one of the boys was at Druimfiaclach collecting the mail and happened there to encounter a party of prospective visitors, he would give elaborately misleading directions as to how to arrive at Camusfeàrna; by these ruses I suspect, our household has forfeited the sympathy of a section of the public, but in order to survive we had no alternative. To not one of these victims of our seeming misanthropy had it occurred, apparently, that they were on holiday and we were not, that each of us had a full day's work to get through as much as, or more than, if we had been holding down an urban office job. We became, in the broadest sense, xenophobe, and resented any intrusion, because each day ended with work undone and a gradually increasing sense of handicap in earning our livings.

There were more precise, definable irritations. Those who were deterred by our final, flaming PRIVATE notices diverted their routes to the surrounding hilltops overlooking Camusfeàrna from a distance of perhaps three hundred yards; from these vantage-points they would scrutinise the house and its environs with field-glasses, telescopes and long-focus ciné-camera lenses, and on one Sunday morning when it was possible to count the heads of five such parties a female guest came to me almost in tears. 'Look,' she said, 'you told me you'd got no sanitation and I said I didn't mind using the countryside – but it's a different thing when four pairs of field-glasses and a ciné-camera are trained on you from all angles.'

What angered me perhaps more than anything else was an incident during the summer of 1961. A very smart small yacht came to anchor in the bay below the house, flying some pennant that was to me unrecognisable. There were three or four very fat men and women aboard. One of the men settled himself in some sort of deck chair in the stern, with a .22 rifle across his knees. His companion began to throw bread to the gulls, and as they alighted on the water in response to this invitation he shot them. We sat at the edge of the sand-dunes and watched. At the end of five minutes I began to grow exceedingly angry; as a blood sport this particular exercise seemed to me despicable. It is academically true that for the protection of other species the greater gulls should be kept within numerical limits, but the method of procedure outraged in me some quite illogical approach to the subject; it seemed wanton and destructive. I sent Jimmy to the house to fetch the .350 big game rifle. When he returned I waited until the fat man had shot a herring gull, and as it drifted away from his yacht, I shot at the dead bird. The noise of that rifle is considerable; the scene dissolved, figures hurried about the deck, the anchor was aweigh and the yacht's auxiliary engines started almost before I had made up my mind to fire another shot astern of her.

The acquisition of my own present motor vessel *Polar Star* was one of the many minor follies with which my life has been sprinkled. When I began to find myself comparatively prosperous it was agreed by my new company, who took over the running of Camusfeàrna, that we had a strong case for a substantial and fast boat. High speed was an absolute necessity, for because of the otters we could never be absent for very long from the house, and distances in the West Highlands are great. Such a boat would, we felt, solve many of our transport and supply problems, and could also be used as emergency accommodation for guests, whose numbers seemed always to increase. The expenditure agreed for this project clearly precluded the purchase of a high-speed luxury yacht; in fact there seemed few craft that would satisfy our requirements for sale at any price. At length an advertisement from a Yorkshire shipyard caught my eye: it read, 'Ex-R.A.F., T.S.D.Y. 1945, 40×9.5×3 ft. draught, diagonal mah. hull, Transom stern, modern bow, twin Perkins 100 h.p. 1952, 20 knots, accommodation four, large cockpit, stated in very good condition, £2,000.' The fact that this miracle was within our agreed price limit should have warned me; I had once before, in the shark fishing years, bought a boat unseen on the strength of the Surveyor's Report, and I should have remembered the deplorable results. It is aggravating to repeat a stupid mistake, and thus to demonstrate that one is slower to learn than many an animal. However, as I could not at the time leave Camusfeàrna, I decided to rely upon an independent surveyor's report, together with advice from expert friends as to the suitability of the type of craft. By them I was advised that no hard chine boat could be expected to stand heavy seas, but that round-bilge construction of equivalent size and speed would be very far beyond the agreed expenditure. I therefore decided to buy the *Polar Star*, subject to a satisfactory survey; apart from a misleading attention to un-important details, the report was excellent, and on July 14th Jimmy Watt left Sandaig for Bridlington to accompany the boat north with her two Yorkshire crew.

The *Polar Star* sailed from Bridlington on July 16th, to pass through the Edinburgh–Glasgow Canal, then the Crinan Canal, through the Mull of Kintyre, and so up the West Coast to Camus-feàrna. The voyage had an inauspicious beginning. The boat was no more than half an hour out from Bridlington when Jimmy saw fierce flames leaping from the stern between the diesel tanks and the calor-gas cylinders. The crew were in the wheelhouse. When Jimmy raised the alarm 'they started charging about all over the ship looking for fire extinguishers, cursing and swearing and expecting an explosion any minute. I had a look myself and there was an extinguisher in the wheelhouse all the time, so I took it and got the fire out myself.' After this mishap she made remarkable progress during the earlier stages of her voyage.

On the third day I was sitting writing at my desk at Camusfeàrna when I found my mind wandering to the probable position of the *Polar Star* at that moment. She must, I decided, be in the Crinan Canal itself – and then a thought came into my head that sent a sharp shock of fear through me. A boat emerging from the Crinan Canal finds itself in the Sound of Jura, almost landlocked, and with only two northward passages to the open sea, those to the north and south of the Island of Scarba. To any uninformed person looking at a chart, the southern passage, between Scarba and Jura, would appear very much the more direct route to clear the southern end of Mull and reach the open sea. That passage, however, is a death-trap, the famous Gulf of Corryvreckan where many, many a boat bigger than the *Polar Star* has met her end in savage whirlpools or the roaring wall of water that is the main overfall. On board the *Sea Leopard* I had watched it from a respectful distance years before, a mad leaping confusion as if the tides of all the world had met in that one place. The C.C.C. Sailing Directions call it 'the worst in the West Highlands . . . at any time there is such risk that it is inadvisable to attempt it'. Now it struck me as just conceivable, but conceivable enough to bring out a fine cold sweat, that the East Coast crew aboard the *Polar Star* had not heard of Corryvreckan and were sailing without proper written directions.

I grabbed the telephone and spoke to the canal authorities at Crinan. The *Polar Star*, they told me, had left the canal some minutes before; I explained my fears, and they offered to try to call her on her radio and telephone back to me. The next quarter of an hour passed slowly at Camusfeàrna, the slower for two incoming calls unconnected with my predicament, in the course of which I was barely able to remain civil. The third time the bell rang it was Crinan and they were reassuring. They had been unable to contact the *Polar Star* because, like much else about her, the radio was out of order, but they had talked with a fishing boat who had seen the *Polar Star*. She had passed, this boat reported, at about twenty-five knots, and appeared to be on course for the

northern channel, not for Corryvreckan. I returned, a little
uneasily, to my work. Jimmy had agreed to telephone from
Mallaig, and that could not be for some hours.

It was late in the evening before he telephoned, and his voice
sounded odd and strained. 'Are you in Mallaig?' I asked.

'No, we're in Tobermory.'

'Tobermory! But you left Crinan hours ago – is everything
all right?'

'Well, not exactly. We ran into some trouble. There's no
glass left in the wheelhouse, for example, and its hatch flaps
have gone too. We ran into a sort of wall of water – like a
head-on collision. Nobody was hurt – much.'

The *Polar Star*'s English crew had indeed steered straight into
the Gulf of Corryvreckan, at its most dangerous of all tides, half
ebb springs, and had charged the main overfall at maximum
speed.

It was not until after Jimmy's arrival that I heard the full story
of this adventure that might so easily have proved tragic. He had
not seen the actual impact, for he had been making tea in the
galley just aft of the wheelhouse. The *Polar Star* was travelling at
full speed, slamming from wave top to wave top as hard chine
boats do, when she seemed to Jimmy to ram something solid.
The teapot was thrown from his hand and he himself was flung
violently against the bulkhead; as this happened a wave of water
some four feet deep swept through the double doors leading into
the wheelhouse. Entrance for'ard thus effectively blocked,
Jimmy made his escape aft. The roll hatch separating the cabin
from the after hold was pulled down against the wind; raising it,
he looked out upon a chaotic sea. It had, he said, no real form or
shape beyond an impression of confused violence, for so many
things appeared to be happening at once; there were fierce down-
sucked whirlpools, waterspouts and waterfalls, and towering
waves truncated at their ends. He climbed out on to the narrow
unrailed side-deck and began precariously to make his way for'ard
to the wheelhouse. While he was doing so the helmsman put the

Polar Star about, still at full speed, and she came round in a wide arc, with seas coming up at her from all sides, from ahead and astern, from port and starboard all at the same time. Once clear of the worst of it Jimmy and one of the two Yorkshiremen worked furiously at the pumps, for the boat was half full of water. Jimmy asked what had happened. 'Dunno – something to do with the wind against the tide, I suppose.'

The *Polar Star* made Tobermory harbour three hours later, and there, past caring for rigid etiquette, her crew picked up the first vacant moorings that held a dinghy, and rowed it ashore.

I was reassured by one thought only; there could be very few vessels of the *Polar Star*'s size that could have attempted that folly and survived it.

The following afternoon the *Polar Star* came up on the southern horizon. Watching her through the field-glasses I could see little but the enormous bow wave she was throwing up; whatever her defects, twenty knots seemed a very conservative estimate of her speed, for from the moment at which she was first visible some ten miles away until she hove to and dropped anchor in the bay was no more than twenty-five minutes.

Terry and I rowed the dinghy out. This was my first sight of my new acquisition, and once aboard her I found it difficult to conceal my disappointment. Potentially, she was all that I had expected, but everything about her reeked of neglect and indifference, from the rusted and functionless instruments on her fascia board, to her uncaulked decks and damp-stained cabin.

As with so many other 'bargains' she required an enormous amount of expenditure before at last she became both trustworthy and socially presentable. At the outset she had, like some aboriginal woman, little but speed and a sound hull; for the rest she was dirty, neglected, squalid in appearance both inside and out, and with a highly unreliable transmission system from the wheel-house to the two big motors in her stern. These were controlled, if the word may be applied to any operation so imprecise, by two throttles on the fascia board, and two gigantic and rusty gear levers not less than four feet high. The neutral position in the forward and backward travel of these monstrosities was exceedingly difficult to achieve, and when found remained, so to speak, an armed neutrality, for the vessel would still creep ahead until the engines were finally stopped. The system was obsolete, and had in recent models been replaced by two small levers on the fascia board, operating a hydraulic gearbox and acting simultaneously as throttle and gear levers. This innovation, we discovered, could only be fitted to the more modern type of engine. In every sphere of life I have always found that one of the most difficult decisions for me has been to determine the moment at which to cut my losses; now, rightly or wrongly, we decided to replace both engines and transmission. We should then have a sound hull and sound engines, and during the winter months we could work at bringing the interior woodwork and fittings up to the same high standard.

This decision, however, we did not take until the autumn; and immediately after her first arrival at Camusfeàrna she had perforce to be sent to the nearest shipyard to remove the evidence of her encounter with Corryvreckan. There she spent some weeks, and we had little use from her that summer; none, in fact, beyond shopping runs to the village, a journey that we found she could accomplish in twelve minutes as opposed to our usual forty by foot-track and road.

August 1961 stands out with a terrible vividness in my mind. Before I began to write this book I wondered whether in the narrative that month should be omitted, whether people who through *Ring of Bright Water* had become vicariously fond of us and of our animals could take even at secondhand the shocks and blows that we sustained, for they came near to bringing about the disintegration of Camusfeàrna as we had known it. The shattering chain of events began with a single episode which, though alarming, did not prepare me for the nightmare that was to follow.

We had staying with us Caroline Jarvis from the London Zoo, who, the previous year, had arranged Terry's employment as an otter-keeper. At that time Edal had the run of the house for most of the day; she would go for her walk in the morning and sleep and play in the living-room; only if there were very many people, or if she was particularly obstreperous would we shut her up in her own quarters, a part of Jimmy's bedroom that he had divided by a four-foot high plasterboard partition. Caroline, who has enormous experience and love of animals of all kinds, got on extremely well with Edal; they had gone for walks together, and only the evening before Edal had gone to sleep on her lap. There was no tension in the atmosphere, nothing to warn us of what was coming.

The next morning Caroline, Jimmy and I set off for a walk with Edal. We had crossed the burn and were walking up the green slope beyond it when I saw Edal, who was close to Caroline, stop suddenly, almost like a pointer, and direct a malevolent glare at Caroline's foot. There was something so unfamiliar in Edal's expression that I called to Caroline to stand still, and hurried towards them. But it was already too late – Edal gave one piercing scream of rage and buried her teeth in Caroline's ankle. Jimmy and I pulled her off and attached a lead to her while Caroline limped home, making light of her injury. Jimmy and I went on with Edal to the islands, discussing all the way the possible reasons for her outrage. At first we were inclined to think that there might be some brain damage remaining from her long illness, but on the veterinary evidence we were forced to discard this theory as untenable. If the nerve itself had been damaged she could never have recovered the full use of her limbs and tail; it must have been the nerve sheath only, and that could not affect her present behaviour. It was, we concluded, some sort of explosion of jealousy; Edal considered herself polyandrously married to Jimmy and myself, and had put Caroline in the position of a rival. We made up our minds not only that she should not meet Caroline again, but that we should be very careful about letting her meet any woman at all. Caroline left two days later; I did not know then that she had given to Terry the thick woollen sweater she had been wearing. I went to London on business for a week, drove north in the Mercedes, and did not get back until after dark on a Monday night.

97

It was so late that I was surprised, as I approached the village pier, to see in the headlights of my car the figures of Jimmy and of Raef Payne, an old friend who had taken over the holiday occupancy of the empty croft adjoining Camusfeàrna. They both looked grave and worried; I knew at once that some sort of disaster had taken place at Camusfeàrna.

It did not take long to say; Terry had been very badly bitten by Edal, and had been taken the previous day to Broadford Hospital on the Isle of Skye. The local doctor had stitched him up as well as she could, but there was the possibility that one finger would have to be amputated. No one seemed to have any very clear idea of how it had happened; Edal had been in her own room, and Terry had gone up to play with her as he often would. He had been entirely alone in the house – Jimmy was out, and Raef had been in his own house a hundred yards away. Both hands were badly damaged. Terry had run over to Raef's house more or less holding on a finger that would otherwise have dropped off.

There was no way for me to get to Skye that night, for it was hours past the time of the last ferry-boat; I would have to wait for the morning. I do not think any of us slept very much.

I went first to see the hospital doctor, so that when I went on from his house to the hospital I was not quite unprepared, for I had been told that Terry might lose one finger on each hand – it depended on how much deterioration there had been overnight. We had agreed that in any case I should bring Terry from the hospital to the doctor's house for a confirmatory examination, that I should bring him home to Camusfeàrna, and that the following day I should drive him to Glasgow for plastic surgery.

When I reached the little hospital I could at first find nobody; the place seemed deserted. I peered this way and that, and at length found myself looking down a corridor to the open door of a ward where a patient was visible sitting up in bed. He was not only sitting up, he was semaphoring wildly with his discarded pyjama-top – suddenly I realised that it was Terry, and that the signals were directed at me. I hurried down the corridor.

There were only two other patients in the ward, an old man and a child, and both were somnolent. Terry could hardly keep his voice down as he demanded over and over again: 'Do I get out of here? Are you going to take me away? You won't leave me here?' At close quarters the smell of gangrene was overpowering; its implications made my voice unsteady as I reassured him.

Back in the doctor's house, I tried to persuade him to close his eyes while his hands were being examined, for I knew by that stench what their appearance would be; but he would have none of it, and took a keen, almost clinical interest in the proceedings. The removal of the bandages revealed a sight so unpleasant that it is better not to attempt description. The top two joints of the second finger of the right hand had literally been chewed off, as had a slightly lesser portion of the same finger of the other hand. The local doctor had somehow contrived to stitch them on again, but now they were very dead indeed. Terry looked at them dispassionately: 'Chop 'em off, Doctor,' he said, 'that ruddy lot's no good to anyone.' Terry was only just fifteen; he never shed one tear either in pain or in self-pity.

The next day we drove to Glasgow, where his father had come to meet him, and he was installed in a nursing home. There he quickly became everybody's pet, and the ten days passed more quickly than he had expected.

When we drove back together to Camusfeàrna we had agreed upon deception for the time being – we were both frightened of the Press getting hold of the story (Edal was at the height of her fame), and also frightened of a local scandal, scandal that might end in her being killed. We owned a portable petrol-driven saw, and outside our circle it was to be given out that Terry had lost his fingers when the chain of this struck a nail in wood and flew off.

I had questioned Terry so closely that he had brought to light the knowledge of which he himself had been unaware – when Edal attacked him he had been wearing Caroline's sweater for the first time. Yet even with this partial solution to her behaviour, the savagery of the attack and the massiveness of the damage made it out of the question for her to meet anyone but Jimmy and myself in the future. It was plain that no amount of attachment to her could justify the risks inherent in her continuing to live in the house and being petted by visitors. If we were to keep her at all there was only one possible course to pursue, and having made the decision we put it into action as quickly as possible. At the seaward side of Camusfeàrna cottage we would erect a prefabricated wooden house at right-angles to it, so that the two formed an L; this new house Edal would share with Jimmy, and through a hatch in its wall she would have permanent access to a spacious enclosure with two pools and every kind of waterworks we could devise. Her living conditions would not be greatly changed, for she could still share Jimmy's bed as was her wont, and she could be taken out for walks on any occasion that the coast (literally) was clear. As an insurance policy against Teko some day surprising us by a similar attack, I decided that he, too, must have a large pool adjoining his lean-to shed.

Jimmy's new house arrived by sea in half a gale of wind, and its unloading presented a weird spectacle as we poled ourselves about on its sections, steering them clear of the rocks and painfully hauling them above the tide's edge. My mind went back to the Island of Soay, and the building of the factory seventeen years earlier; I realised that once again, as if it were an inescapable pattern, I was in the initial stages of constructing and maintaining a complex organisation on an almost impossibly remote site.

When the building was finally erected, decorated and furnished, it made an imposing room, thirty feet long by twelve feet wide, with eight large windows. The furthest ten feet were divided by a waist-high partition to form a bedroom for both Jimmy and Edal, and, since she was now to have permanent access to water and we could not dry her every time she emerged from it, we adopted the technique of an infra-red lamp hanging above a bed of towels just inside the hatch. This extremely practical idea had not, in fact, been ours in invention; it had been devised by one of the few other people in the British Isles who keep otters, Mr Jeremy Harris, and it ensured that the otter's bedding would always be dry whether or not there was a human in attendance.

At this point, while I am describing what may appear an excessive concern for Edal's comfort and well-being, I should perhaps explain my own attitude towards her in the light of all that had taken place. She had inflicted terrible damage on someone for whom I was responsible and of whom I was fond, but for several seemingly valid reasons I did not feel I could send her away. Any private home to which she went would be exposed to the same risk, and it seemed an act of wanton cruelty to send this house-living animal to a life sentence behind the prison bars of a zoo. She was extremely and affectionately attached to Jimmy and to myself; she had acted instinctively; moreover, it was in some sense to the exploitation of her person in print that I owed my present prosperity. There will, no doubt, be those who feel these loyalties to be misguided; I can only say that in our own minds we had no option.

The prefabricated house was the easiest part of our plan to put into operation, though it involved much time, labour and expense; the installation of pools of the size we felt to be necessary was a very much more formidable task. In broad principle there are two main types of swimming-pool marketed for use in, say, suburban gardens; those which are circular, made of sectional steel sheeting standing upright upon the ground and holding a giant bag of waterproof material, and those which are rectangular, made of some such substance as fibre-glass, designed to be sunk into a prepared pit of the same dimensions. Both are almost unbelievably costly, but of the two the sheet-metal-and-bag type is less so. This, in view of the general heavy outlay, decided us upon the wrong choice, and we ordered three, two of four yards diameter and one of six yards. One small and one large were to be installed at different levels, partially sunk, in Edal's new quarters, and the third was to be erected in a new enclosure surrounding Teko's house, in case he too should at some time in the future have to be treated with caution.

Teko's pool burst on the first day that it was filled with water, and, being immediately outside my ground-floor window, it flooded the house with all its four thousand gallons. It did more, for it laid flat the wooden paling of the enclosure, and had Terry, who was standing beside the pool, not seen the metal beginning to bulge, he might well have been killed. The containing wall of the pool burst on that side only, and I think my calculations are conservative when I say that the metal sheets must have been slammed down by not less than twenty tons of water. A week later we replaced the wreckage by a sunk fibre-glass tank sixteen feet by eight by four-and-a-half feet deep. This object, looking like a giant's washing-up basin, arrived by the usual combination of rail and boat travel, and was delivered in Camusfeàrna south bay by a hired launch. (The *Polar Star* was absent, as so often that summer, undergoing some minor surgery to her fuel system.)

Edal's pools were partially sunk, and boarded outside to resemble huge vats; in their case there was no such disaster as had occurred with Teko's, but she began early to take a mischievous delight in ripping the P.V.C. lining with her teeth, so that the level of the water could never be relied upon, and the complicated system of syphon and waterfall that we had devised was rarely in working order. We had, nevertheless, solved the problem of her continued existence at Camusfeàrna.

6

The Wreck of the Polar Star

SATURDAY, October 7th 1961, began in a calm and orderly manner and ended in chaos. The events of the evening formed one of the chain of disasters, greater or lesser, that have punctuated the attempt to make Camusfeàrna, in all its isolation, a place of semi-permanent residence. At some time in the morning Miss Jean Alexander, who manages the Invermoriston Hotel, telephoned to say that she had staying with her Mr Lionel Edwards, known to several generations as a painter of hunting scenes, together with his daughter and son-in-law. Mr Edwards was particularly anxious to visit Camusfeàrna and see the otters, but he was by now a man in old age, and the long, steep track between Druimfiaclach and Camusfeàrna was beyond his capacity. The visit was possible only if we could take the *Polar Star* to the village pier four miles away and collect him there, returning him in the evening to the same place where his car would be waiting. There appeared no possible reason against this; the weather was flat calm with intermittent light rain and we had nothing on hand but the normal routine of the household. We arranged to collect Mr Edwards's party from the pier at about two-thirty.

Everything went smoothly until the visitors, who had lingered long watching Edal and Teko disporting themselves in their respective pools, began their homeward journey in the evening, and even then I was unaware of anything amiss. We cast off the *Polar Star*'s moorings at about a quarter past six; it was a dull grey evening with heavy rain hammering down on to a completely smooth sea, and there was not a whisper of wind from any quarter. There were some parcels to be fetched from the village, and it was dusk before Jimmy, Terry, and I set out again for home, the beginning of one of the worst nights I can remember.

The very high speed of the *Polar Star* reduces the time necessary for the journey to a little over ten minutes and we used all her speed because I thought that the very poor visibility might make it difficult to find our moorings; I was the more concerned when as we approached the Camusfeàrna islands I saw patches of dense grey mist. There was still no breath of wind to disperse them, and still the vertical rain streamed down and hissed into an unmoving sea; it was with real relief that I saw the big white buoy loom up through the mist no more than ten yards ahead. Jimmy and Terry lifted it aboard. I saw from their gestures that something was wrong, but the continuous rasping screech of the clear-glass circle in the windscreen made it impossible to hear their voices. Then Jimmy came down through the wheelhouse hatch. 'There's no dinghy on the moorings – just a cut end of rope!'

It was clear to me at once what had happened; I had been careless for the first time, and must have cut the rope with one of the *Polar Star*'s propellers as we left for the village. The full gravity of the situation did not immediately strike me; in that dead calm sea it seemed easy enough to calculate the drift of the dinghy during the hour of our absence and to recover her by one means or another. The only real trouble at this stage was the mist and the increasing darkness in a spot so strewn with rock and reef. The tide had been ebbing for nearly an hour and a half, which meant that in the absence of any wind the dinghy should have drifted southward and come ashore somewhere on the lighthouse island, whose dark bulk was by now only faintly discernible against the clouded night sky. The only point on the whole island where it might even theoretically be practicable to land one of the boys was at the lighthouse itself, where two L-shaped lengths of heavy-gauge piping led down into the water to form a rough-and-ready pier usable at any tide higher than three-quarter ebb springs. On one engine and minimum possible revs I crept cautiously round the north end of the island; the searchlight lit only a solid wall of rain, and as the lighthouse came into view its flashes seemed like torchlight shining on fountain spray, lighting nothing below them. We were no more than five yards from the pipes before I could make them out in the thin light of Terry's torch, and it was a tribute as much to his agility as to my manoeuvring that he contrived to scramble ashore while with enormous relief I put the engine astern. It was about then that I realised that this was the darkest night I had ever seen.

Terry's task was tough even for one who had not had two fingers amputated only a few weeks before. He was to search the northern shore of the island with its thousand weed-covered outcrops and treacherous crevices, and if he found the dinghy he was to bring it where we would lie at anchor as near to our moorings as we could judge. If he found nothing, he was to wait until nearly midnight, wade waist-deep to the next island in the chain, and so to Camusfeàrna south bay, where the tiny pram dinghy was drawn up on the sand beach. From there it would be a two-mile row right round the south side of the islands to reach where we lay at anchor, but at least the sea was so far in our favour. We had chosen Terry for this role because his hands made it difficult for him to handle anchor or rope, while his rowing was little affected.

Jimmy and I returned to the north side of the island and dropped anchor, though by now the darkness was so total that, with the lighthouse obscured by the headland, we had little real idea of our position. At first we thought we could make out the faint flicker of a torch from time to time on the island shore, but then everything was black outside the lit cockpit of the *Polar Star* and the only sound was that of the rain. So it was for an hour or more; then came the first whine of wind in the rigging of the wireless mast, and a little later the first slap of breaking water on the ship's side. The wind was southerly and we were lying in shelter; it was plain now that Terry's alternative course, to row the pram round the lee shore of the islands in pitch darkness, would be little less than suicidal. Jimmy and I conferred, and decided to take the *Polar Star* round to the south bay and anchor her there, so that Terry, if he could launch the pram at all, would have but a short row out to us. It was then a little after half past nine.

We weighed anchor and very gingerly we set off again. It was as if one were deprived of all one's useful senses – the utter enveloping blackness and the deafening scream of the clear-glass combined to produce a sensation of claustrophobia such as I have never before experienced. I wanted to shout 'Let me out of here! Let me out of here!' We passed well to the west of the lighthouse and kept on southward for what I thought an amply safe distance before turning up for the south bay; but, no doubt subconsciously accustomed to the *Polar Star*'s normal high speed, I overestimated the distance we had covered. The lighthouse was obscured by the headland, and the only visible thing outside the wheelhouse was the intermittent pinprick of another lighthouse miles to the south-west.

I did have a split second of warning, but it was too brief to be of any value. The searchlight had shone only upon the unvarying wall of rain; now, only feet from our bows, I had a sickening camera-shutter image of solid rock. Then we struck and struck hard, and the bows reared. Both engines full astern produced only a hideous grinding sound, and after a few seconds we stopped them.

The worst of it was that we had no clear idea of our position, nor whether we were aground on an island or a reef. The whole of the area of the Camusfeàrna islands is a death-trap, even in daylight, to any boat unfamiliar with it; now, with more than four hours ebb tide, we might be on any one of fifty rocks. The *West Coast Pilot* with an inspired typographical slip, describes the south side of the islands as 'foul fround', and never had the fround seemed fouler than now with the *Polar Star* hard aground in the middle of a black night and a rising wind.

When I went aft I thought the hull was holed, for the floorboards were awash, but then I saw that the angle at which her bows had reared must have sent all the bilge water to the stern and that this might be no more than the accumulation of rainwater over many hours of downpour. We decided to try to explore our surroundings, and we clambered overboard, Jimmy holding the head rope and I the stern. The rock shelved steeply and it was slippery and weed-covered; feeling upward in the darkness there was only more weed. We did little speculation aloud as to our whereabouts, for the evidence so far pointed to a reef, and neither Jimmy nor I could swim. There was one life-jacket in the *Polar Star*, and Terry had the other.

The wind rose steadily and the waves came out of the dark and broke over us, and as they grew greater they broke, too, over the *Polar Star*'s starboard quarter, so that she began to ship green water into the after cockpit. Then she began to bump and slam upon the rock that was holding her, and it was clear that she would break up if she stayed where she was. We went back aboard her and tried the engines again; she would not move, but there seemed a faint chance that if we were both ashore on the rock we might push her off on the crest of a wave to take her chance of finding sand or gravel. We pumped her bilges, and for another despairing half hour we struggled in the slimy seaweed and the breaking waves until at length a slight veer in the wind did our work for us and suddenly she was free. All we had salvaged from her was a boat-hook. Our watches had stopped owing to immersion, but I think it was then about eleven o'clock. As the *Polar Star* drifted away from us we both felt very desolate.

We were surprised by how quickly her mast-light was obscured – no piece of rock formation that we could visualise could have hidden her so quickly, but by now it was almost dead low tide, and this was no guarantee that we were not on a reef. We could explore only by touch, for the blackness was utter and complete; passing one's hand before one's eyes they registered no faintest change of shade. Jimmy said: 'This is what it must be like to be blind, stone blind.'

The first thing seemed to be to get above the waves; this was no very logical process of reasoning, for we had no inch of dry clothing between us, and the rain was now lashing in on a force six southerly wind. The first ten feet were almost vertical and all weed-covered, and we could only raise ourselves almost inch by inch. More weed and more; I began to have a chilling certainty that we must be on a reef and not an island, and high tide would be before dawn. A small glow of hope warmed us when my hand touched the roughness of rock for the first time, but it was barnacles that I felt beneath my finger-tips. Jimmy found bare dry rock first, but it was smooth and sheer and he could find no fingerhold. He felt out to the left with his foot and there was nothing there; I did the same to my right and found nothing either. We were evidently climbing some sort of narrow buttress. I remember saying: 'There just isn't a piece of rock like this anywhere round Camusfeàrna.'

That first twenty or thirty feet until we came suddenly on rough, tussocky grass must have taken us more than half an hour. We went on climbing, grass, rock, then grass again. Jimmy said suddenly: 'There's only one piece of ground like this – we're at the gull colony on the south face of the Lighthouse Island. I bet that in another quarter of an hour we'll see the lighthouse.' We did, and we were safe, but our troubles had only begun.

Even in the best of daylight conditions, the traverse of the half-mile length of the Lighthouse Island is no easy matter, for it is one of the roughest, toughest pieces of ground that may be conceived. Its uneven, rocky shore is split by deep fissures many feet deep, and these are camouflaged, as are pitfall traps for wild animals, by a rank growth of heather and briar. Above the shore-line the surface is never even; it is as though a truddle of big boulders had been flung together by some giant and then roughly coated over with the coarsest vegetation available to the climate. There are patches of dense, waist-high scrub willow through which it is entirely impossible to force a passage; ankle-twisting areas of tussock grass where each football-sized clump is as hard at its base as a stone; rooty heather growing three feet and more from treacherous holes and gulleys; and, worst of all, bramble thickets like barbed-wire entanglements. When in summer we would come here to count the eider ducks' nests or harvest herring gull eggs we would pick our way with difficulty through this defensive jungle and often have to retrace our footsteps and seek a new path through the undergrowth; now we were confronted with the whole length of the island without even the use of our eyes. Also we were in a hurry now, both because of the urgency of calling salvage to the *Polar Star* and because soon the depth of water would increase between us and the next island of the chain.

We joined hands like children, and with Jimmy in the lead with the boat-hook we began to feel our way forward foot by foot. We stumbled and fell and swore, the briars tore at our legs and we bruised our shins and twisted our ankles among the rocks, and our teeth were chattering and all the time the rain came deluging in on the south wind; it ran in at our collars and trickled out into our shoes, and there was no speck of illumination in all the black night. Before each step forward Jimmy felt ahead of him with the boat-hook; it was fifteen feet long, but often it touched nothing and we had to skirt our way along the edge of a long rock-fissure only to find ourselves brought up short again by the density of undergrowth. At some point in this nightmare journey, we came into sight of a small white light that could only be the mast-light of the *Polar Star*; it seemed stationary, but we found it impossible to estimate the distance or judge whether she was on rock or soft beach. It must have taken us the best part of an hour to reach the north-eastern tip of the island, from which by wading we might gain the next, and by that time both of us were very near to the stage at which it seems simpler to lie down and give up. Of Terry we had heard nothing, and it would be superfluous to add that we had seen nothing.

The water between the islands was chest-high; sometimes, when our feet slipped deep among the weedy rocks, it was head-high and we were floundering. Jimmy led me on by the hand, feeling his way before him with the boat-hook, and it struck me what a bizarre spectacle we would present if some miracle could suddenly lift the darkness and leave us flooded with light.

'Even the weariest river winds somewhere safe to sea', and it was where the Camusfeàrna burn does this that there occurred the artistically climactic incident of the night. We had been on flat grassy ground for some minutes when I heard in front of us the familiar sound of the burn running over shingle and boulders; I forsook Jimmy's guiding hand, and shouting: 'We've done it!

We're saved!', I stepped briskly forward. Never had pride a swifter fall; I had been at the very brink of the low sand cliff where the sand martins breed, and I stepped straight into space to fall ten feet and land on my head. For the first time that night I was truly unconscious for a little while, to be brought round by the full weight of Jimmy's boot on my face.

Terry reached the house perhaps half an hour after we did, and he had passed as bad a time or worse; for he had been for even longer without light. All hopes of finding the dinghy had ended abruptly and painfully after the first ten minutes, when a long slithering fall among the slimy rocks of the tide-line had smashed the torch and hurt the newly healed stumps of his fingers. He went on searching in the dark, hoping to stumble on the dinghy by accident, but he only stumbled on everything else. He saw us begin to move the *Polar Star* from where we had her anchored, and feeling the freshening wind he guessed our purpose. He began to cross the island to put his alternative plan into action, but without the aid of the boat-hook that had saved us from broken limbs, he fared worse and his progress was even slower than ours. When at last he was on the south side of the island he saw the mast-head light of the *Polar Star*, stationary perhaps a quarter of a mile from him, but no port or starboard lights. At first he could not bring himself to believe that she had been abandoned; then he tried to visualise her position, and realised that she must be aground. He had a life-jacket and he tried to swim to her, but he was exhausted and beginning to feel the effects of exposure, so he dragged himself ashore on the first piece of land he could reach. This was another island, if possible rougher and more inhospitable than the Lighthouse Island, and it took him some time to recognise where he was. By the time he reached Camus-feàrna he was far gone, but still as indomitably cheerful as his chattering teeth would permit him.

As soon as I had reached the house I had telephoned to Bruce Watt, who had long ago been skipper of my shark-fishing vessel the *Sea Leopard*, and who now possessed three sizeable boats for the diversion of tourists. He was also coxswain of Mallaig lifeboat. For purposes of report to the necessary authorities the events of that interminable night were condensed into two brief reports, one by myself and one by him:

'Report on Abandoning of Polar Star'

'On Saturday October 7th I took a party of visitors in the *Polar Star* from my moorings N.E. of the Camusfeàrna Islands, to the village pier, some four miles up the Sound of Sleat, accompanied by two employees, J. M. Watt and T. P. Nutkins. Weather conditions when I left moorings at 6.45 p.m. were flat calm with heavy rain and poor visibility, tide approximately at half hour's ebb. I left the pier for the return journey at approximately 7.20 p.m. and arrived at my moorings a little after 7.30 p.m. It was then after dusk; there was a thick local mist and continuous small rain. On picking up my mooring buoy I found that my dinghy was not on the moorings and that the dinghy's painter had been cut, leaving some two feet attached to the mooring-rope. Visibility at this time was some 15 yards. Tide (two knots) being stronger than wind, it appeared possible that the dinghy was on the north-facing shore of the Lighthouse Island, which is steep-to but not clean. I succeeded in putting Nutkins ashore at the Lighthouse, where an arrangement of heavy-gauge piping forms a pier which is usable until three-quarter ebb springs. Nutkins was instructed to look for the dinghy and, if he failed to find it, to wait until he could reach the mainland by wading waist-deep and fetch a second dinghy (pram) from Camusfeàrna South Bay. Owing to visibility conditions, no contact with Nutkins was possible after he was put ashore. *Polar Star* remained on anchor E.N.E. of Camusfeàrna Lighthouse. At approximately 9.30 p.m. it began to blow force 5–6 southerly with heavy rain and practically nil visibility, and it was plain that the passage of the pram from Camusfeàrna South Bay round the lee lighthouse point would be dangerous to Nutkins. I therefore decided to take *Polar Star* round into the South Bay to shorten the row for Nutkins as much as possible. I proceeded on the starboard engines only at 600 r.p.m., approximately 3 knots. After Camusfeàrna Lighthouse was obscured, visibility was literally nil and heavy rain rendered the searchlight useless. No light was visible except

Halstray Lighthouse, $3\frac{1}{4}$ miles W.S.W. At approximately 10.15 p.m. I struck a reef, and, despite putting both engines full astern immediately, remained fast. Investigation revealed a rock, dry about one fathom, on our port side, but owing to foul ground all the way S.E. of the Lighthouse Island, I was unable to determine our exact position. Wind was approximately force 6 southerly; *Polar Star*'s port side began to slam on the rock and she appeared certain to break up unless freed. She was also shipping green water over the starboard gunwale aft. She would not drive off on the propellers, but there seemed a small chance of pushing her off on a wave crest if Watt and myself were both ashore on the rock. I therefore decided to try this, on the chance of her subsequently being driven ashore on sand or gravel, rather than the certainty of her breaking up where she was. After pumping her, and after a long time of trying, we succeeded in pushing her off as the result of a slight veer in the wind, and she began to drift N.E. From the moment she was free, there was no means of regaining the vessel. Our watches had stopped owing to immersion, but I should estimate the time at approximately 11.00 p.m. Watt and I made shore after the greatest difficulty and arrived at the house at 12.45 a.m. I immediately telephoned to Mr Bruce Watt, coxswain of Mallaig lifeboat, who also regularly undertakes salvage with his own craft.

'Nutkins was not able to wade from the Lighthouse Island until 11.30 p.m., and visibility was so poor that he did not reach the house until after our arrival.

'I do not know how Mr Bruce Watt effected the salvage, but at first light in the morning he had the *Polar Star* alongside his boat, *Western Isles*, on my moorings. He then removed *Polar Star* to Mallaig.

'The dinghy was recovered $4\frac{1}{2}$ miles N. on the afternoon of the same day.

'*Gavin Maxwell.*'

'*Report on Salvaging of* Polar Star'

'At 0045 hours on Sunday October 8th 1961 Major Gavin Maxwell phoned myself (Bruce Watt) to say that his vessel the

Polar Star was ashore to the East of Camusfeàrna Lighthouse and that he and his crew had managed to get ashore on the lighthouse island. He had left a light burning in the *Polar Star* and hoped that we would arrive in time to salvage her.

'I dressed immediately and went down to my ship, the *Western Isles* and sailed at 0115 hrs. The night was extremely dark with showers of rain and winds of force 5–6 S.E. to S.

'At 0230 hrs on approaching Camusfeàrna Lighthouse, we observed a small light to the approximate East of the said lighthouse. On account of the darkness of the night and foul waters we were unable to approach any further and decided to go round to the lee of the lighthouse and anchor the *Western Isles*; and then to get ashore with the dinghy and investigate the position of the *Polar Star* and the possibilities of salvaging her. On getting ashore, we carefully made our way to the windward side and by torch light observed that the *Polar Star* was aground on a rock just breaking surface about 10 yds. from the main reef. The boat was unmoored and abandoned. The *Polar Star* was aground forward with her stern rising and falling with the incoming surf.

'We decided that something would have to be done quickly if the boat was to be salvaged as the weather was deteriorating with the flood tide. We made our way back to the *Western Isles* as quickly as possible and came round to the windward side of the lighthouse where we sounded our way into a suitable position and dropped anchor. We fell in towards the casualty and rode to 30 fathoms of cable. When we felt sure that our anchor was holding, a crew member left with the dinghy to pass a rope to the *Polar Star*. With great difficulty a noose was passed over the winch on the bow of the *Polar Star* and the crew member returned to the *Western Isles*.

'Conditions by this time had steadily worsened and the *Polar Star* was now beam on to the rocks on her port side and bumping heavily. We moved slowly ahead with the *Western Isles* and at the same time winching in our anchor cable. The *Polar Star* by now had come head to wind and after a few minutes pause finally came clear.

'With great difficulty, owing to the *Polar Star*'s sheering and

113

extremely bad visibility, we managed to get her round to the lee side of the lighthouse island and moor her alongside the *Western Isles*. During this operation it was observed that in the after well of the *Polar Star* there was several fathoms of rope with one end of it attached to the boat and the other to an oil drum. This we assumed was to have acted as a marker should the vessel sink. The time now being approximately 0500 hrs, we rested and awaited daylight.

'After daylight, when we were trying to assess the seaworthiness of the casualty and what damage had been sustained, Major Maxwell and his crew hailed us by megaphone from the shore.

'We rowed across to Major Maxwell and it was decided that the *Polar Star* should be towed to Mallaig.

'The following Tuesday, owing to the slipway being full, she was beached on wooden battens and the extent of the damage investigated. As far as could be seen by ourselves, Lloyd's agents and the local carpenter the damage was as follows:

'Both propellers buckled.
'Port A bracket supporting propeller and shaft strained and pushed upwards into the skin.
'Keel badly chafed and strained.
'Planking chafed, very deeply in places.
'Port chine strake loosened.
'Approx. 2 ft of Keel knocked out of fore foot.
'Hull generally strained and leaking.

'*Bruce Watt*.'

7

Teko Revisited

It was well that we had given thought to the possibility, however improbable it appeared then, that the friendly, bouncing, affectionate Teko might one day commit the same outrage as had Edal, for by the time it did happen we were entirely prepared. He had his own heated house, his own enclosure and pool, and it had been planned in such a way that a dividing gate could exclude him from either one or the other. In emergency, he could be tended by the most timorous.

The emergency was not, in fact, long in coming. In November I became engaged to be married, and in December my future wife, Lavinia, and stepchildren Nicholas and Simon Renton came to Camusfeàrna for part of the Christmas holidays.

Terry was at that time still looking after Teko and taking him for his daily walk, in company with the deerhound Dirk. Dirk was a comparatively recent acquisition, a gigantic yearling standing nearly forty inches at the shoulder, and it had been a joy to discover that he and Teko regarded each other as natural playmates, Dirk making rings of dazzling speed around the otter, or leaping over him high in the air. Simon, then aged thirteen, had accompanied the party more than once, and Teko had given him no more than a casual and friendly greeting as they set off.

As in the case of Edal and Caroline, the attack came without warning or apparent reason, and not long after they had left the house. They were on their way to the island beaches, and Simon was walking a little in front; the two animals, who had not yet begun to romp seriously, were walking sedately between him and Terry. Suddenly something detonated in Teko's brain – akin, I am certain, to Edal's past explosions of jealousy. He flew at Simon from behind, knocked him down (it must be remembered that Teko weighed little less than fifty pounds) and bit him savagely in the thigh. It was not just a single bite, it was a sustained attack, that might have been extremely serious had not Terry done a flying rugger tackle and pulled him off by the tail. It was the first of two rescues carried out by Terry after he had lost his own fingers. Teko responded instantly to Terry's authority; there was at no moment any sign of the attack changing direction from Simon to himself.

From what emotional rag-bag these outbursts are pulled it is impossible to say with any certainty, but I am convinced that the emotion is basically that which we describe as jealousy. To the otters, Caroline and Simon were interlopers; the otters sensed, if it is permissible to anthropomorphise so far, that something they had regarded as being their exclusive right was being shared with a stranger.

The immediate consequences of this incident were less grave than might have been feared, and were greatly helped toward this end by Simon's cavalier attitude to his injuries. He was unable to play football for a week after going back to school, and he will never lose the scars, but, like Terry, he shed no tear and made no complaint.

I left Camusfeàrna for London on January 19th, to be married on February 1st, and on the 22nd Teko attacked Jimmy. He and Terry had taken Teko and Dirk for a walk, and as usual the dog and the otter had indulged in wild games in and out of the sea. They had begun to walk home, Jimmy leading with Dirk and Terry following with Teko. Jimmy stopped for a moment to pat and caress the dog, and in that instant Teko flew at him from behind. The first deep bite was in the calf of the leg, but by the time Jimmy had realised that Teko's rage was too great to yield to any persuasion, he had received other severe bites in the shin and the foot. Jimmy did the only thing he could do; he ran for it, with Teko in close pursuit. Normally he would have outdistanced Teko quickly, but he was handicapped both by his injuries and by heavy boots, and he fell once, to realise as he recovered himself that Teko was almost upon him and that Terry was still some yards behind. By now this demoniac and breathless procession had reached a point immediately above the small sand cliff where the sand martins breed, the point from which I had fallen on the night we abandoned the *Polar Star*; and Jimmy, remembering that Teko had always evinced a dislike of heights, jumped from this cliff and floundered across the burn. The moment's pause that this manoeuvre had given Teko had been time enough for Terry to overtake him and attach his lead. Jimmy was in a state of virtual collapse at the other side of the burn.

All this was kept secret from me until my return to Camusfeàrna sixteen days later.

Terry is convinced that this disaster too was due to jealousy, that there existed some close bond between dog and otter, and that Teko saw this relationship threatened by Jimmy's apparent affection for the dog. It was Jimmy, in any case, who was in that situation the outsider; both Teko and Dirk were specifically under Terry's charge, and the three formed in some sense an independent unit.

Whatever the reason, I was faced on my return with a situation not easy of solution. I was to leave for North Africa in the near future; during my absence only Terry could look after Teko, and only Jimmy could look after Edal. If either of them were ill one otter would have to be treated as a zoo animal, tended without contact. I had become, and remain, the only person who trusted both otters and had no reason to fear either of them.

There have been times when, despite their consistently affectionate attitude to me, it has been difficult to forget the terrible injuries they have inflicted upon others. These moments have arisen mainly with Teko. He has always possessed a genius for removing his harness and an intense dislike for having it refitted, which is in itself an exceedingly difficult task when the otter is uncooperative. Teko resists the operation with all his really enormous strength and eel-like sinuosity, accompanying his motor actions with vocalisation calculated to intimidate the most courageous. His sound of displeasure is an essentially cockney vowel sound 'wow-wow-wow', each syllable prolonged and yelled out somewhere in the middle range of a tenor's voice; there have been times when I have almost expected this to change suddenly into the scream that accompanies an attack, but I have at no moment truly lost the sensation of mastery in which lies my salvation. The occasion when I have come nearest to doing so was in the autumn of 1962, when Terry, who had by that time given up looking after otters and was engaged entirely upon the construction of new buildings, came to tell me that Teko had a terrible wound. This proved not to be an exaggeration – it was an enormous incision that looked as if it could only have been made with a scalpel as a first stage to removing the limb, and it stretched from under the arm almost to the shoulder. Behind the elbow, where the forelimb joins the body, an otter has a great baggy fold of skin which becomes almost like a wing when the limb is extended forward; this had been cut right through to reveal not only flesh but sinew. The wound was at least three inches deep and, because a side-strap of the harness had sunk right into its depths, it was gaping four inches wide. Seen in profile as he stood on his hind legs, the whole animal looked as if he had virtually been cut in two.

The first task was clearly to remove the harness, and I was the only one of us who could attempt it. Knowing that Teko must be in great pain, and remembering how much he hated his harness being handled even without this added stimulus to anger, I thought it very probable that my moment had come; it was, however, impossible to leave him in his present condition. (It may be worth mentioning that no form of thigh-boot or glove provides any protection, as armour, against an otter that is attacking with serious intent.) It would clearly be impracticable to hold him in such a way as to undo the two buckles securing the harness, and the material itself was of extremely hard nylon so that I did not think it possible to cut through with a single stroke of any blade that I had; moreover, any sawing action would necessarily drag the strap deeper and deeper into the flesh. In the end I settled for the kitchen scissors, and I entered his enclosure trying consciously to repress the fear that I felt, for however the emotion of fear is communicated to an animal the fact of its communication is unquestionable and disastrous.

Teko stood up and put his forepaws against me – they reached almost to my hip – and whimpered. I put my face down to his and spoke consoling, caressing words to him while my hands were busy about his shoulder, trying to work the scissor blade under the nylon. It cut slowly, but it cut; after the first strap gave way there was a second, and then finally I had to pull the shoulder-strap out of the wound in which it was deeply embedded – throughout all this Teko made not one single angry sound.

For eight days thereafter I had to go into his house and treat the wound by blowing powder deep into the sulcus, and though my manipulations must have been exceedingly painful he made no demonstration of protest whatsoever. (As a further safeguard against infection we put an enormous hunk of rock salt in his pool; this fascinated him beyond measure, and at the end of the first hour he had somehow contrived to hoist the whole forty-pound lump to the surface and to manhandle it out of the water on to the bank .Then he put it back and repeated the performance.)

Whereas Teko always gives me delighted welcome when I return after absence from Camusfeàrna, repeating again and again his greeting sound of 'whack-o, whack-o', Edal would as invariably shrill her rebukes to myself or Jimmy for a desertion of even a day or two. (At first I was at a loss to interpret this phenomenon, and it was not until recently that I learnt that it is commonly recognised among human infants, the form of protest ranging between behaviour superficially akin to Edal's and enuresis; the rebuke, when it is not overtly expressed, is implicit.) Edal would wail and snarl and lie on her back scrabbling at the air with her hands, her voice a shrewish and feminine variation upon Teko's, lacking the consonant but retaining the cockney intonation, so that it emerges as 'ow-ow-ow', with a richness of disyllabic vowel-sound that might have baffled Professor Higgins had he encountered it in Eliza Doolittle. It was not until whichever of us had been absent had adequately apologised for his inconstancy that she would abandon her outraged attitude and seek the reassurance of caressing hands. What, one asks oneself, would Lovelace have felt had Lucasta's only reaction to his poem (and, after all, Edal enjoyed not only four brief verses but several thousand words of prose) been 'ow-ow-ow' until he said it was all untrue and he was never going away again?

It is an appropriate moment to place on record an unpalatable opinion, in which I hope that I may be proved wrong. Whatever may be true of other species, I do not believe that any fully adult otter of that to which Edal and Teko belong is to be trusted completely with any human other than its acknowledged foster-parents. The emotions are too intense, the degree of affection accorded by the otter too profound. To achieve placidity, to enjoy to the full the company of one of these wholly fascinating creatures one would have perforce to live the life of a hermit, with only animal companionship.

Edal and Teko will not, I think, have forfeited the final sympathy of their fans by the momentary violence that I have described. They acted instinctively and within the framework of their heritage, a framework in which violence was essential to survival and reproduction. It is not the existence of these explosions that should excite attention and comment, but that a carnivorous wild animal, never domesticated in the early history of mankind as were the wild dogs, should in the first generation of captivity or other association with man display so much that he finds acceptable and approvable. Several million people responded sympathetically to these aspects of Mijbil and Edal, described without selection or rejection of fact, and those with any sincerity should respond with understanding to the whole character of the creature as it emerges into maturity. An animal, like a human, who displays nothing but charm becomes insipid. ('I was right years ago,' said Anthony Blanche, the archetype of articulacy in Mr Evelyn Waugh's *Brideshead Revisited*, 'when I *warned* you. I took you out to dinner to warn you of charm.' Sebastian Flyte, against whom the tirade is directed, never escapes from the narrow confines of his charm; the only positive action of which he is capable is that of self destruction, that of dying as a dypso-maniac in a North African monastery.) Any wild animal displaying nothing but charm is doomed, metaphorically, to the same end, and by the same process of denying his instinctive needs. In either case we must pose a pattern of behaviour desired by the majority – in Sebastian's case that of the English Roman Catholic Church in which he had been indoctrinated; that, in particular, of a prominent *clique* whose actions were subject to the super-ego of Farm Street. I am aware that to many this equation of humans, with their various religious criteria of behaviour, with the animal situation when interfered with by a 'master' set of rules equally unrelated to instinct, will appear both offensive and ridiculous, but the parallel is valid. Had Edal and Teko not allowed liberty to instinct they would in time have shed the rest of their positive qualities as well and have been left with nothing but charm.

8

Accident, Fire and Flood

WE had little use from the *Polar Star* during the autumn months; what time was not taken up by repairs after her wreck and the fitting of her new engines was filled, for the most part, by gales and heavy seas.

Meanwhile, before she could be brought ashore in February, we had to arrange the building of a cradle for her, for she could not be beached in the ordinary way without damage to her propeller-shafts. A wheeled cradle to carry a boat of nine tons deadweight is a substantial vehicle, costly to construct and exceedingly difficult to transport to a site as remote as Camusfeàrna. Ours was built on the Clyde, some 250 road miles to the south of us, and carried by heavy lorry to the village pier five miles away; from there we hired one of the semi-local car-ferry boats to bring the massive structure in sections to the south bay at low tide.

The cradle had then to be assembled in shallow water before the tide rose; the whole operation had to be timed with military precision, for the *Polar Star*, lying seventeen miles to the southward, was to be floated on to her cradle as the tide came up. The whole eleven tons we then intended to winch up the beach and on to the grass beside the house, using for this purpose our own Sahara Land Rover. The car was already at the house, for, after the narrative of *Ring of Bright Water* had been brought to a close, the proprietors of the estate on whose land Camusfeàrna lies had decided to bulldoze a track to a neighbouring bay, and we had paid for three extra days bulldozing to branch this track to

Camusfeàrna. The result could hardly be called a road; in places, indeed, the bulldozer seemed to have succeeded merely in removing the floating crust from stretches of peat bog, but by Land Rover the track was usable after a spell of dry weather, when its gradient of one in three was not mud-covered nor its flatter stretches reduced by rain to seemingly bottomless morass. The downward journey was usually practicable in theory, though the fording of the Camusfeàrna burn, which cut the upper section of the track, was difficult in spate; but to ascend in anything but the dryest conditions we had become used to putting out anchors ahead of the Land Rover and hauling her up on her own winch. Certain sections of the track were by now littered with broken anchor flukes in evidence of past failure.

Our plans did not run with clockwork efficiency. The two-ton cradle came apart as it was dropped into the sea, and its massive metal parts proved very difficult to reassemble in the water. When Jimmy Watt in the Land Rover began to winch it to the position chosen for floating-on, the *Polar Star* was still on the horizon, but long before we were ready she was cruising impatiently round the bay. It was a further two hours before she settled solidly on to the heavy timbers of her cradle, and our work was only begun.

The Land Rover was able to move the whole eleven tons a hundred yards up the beach to the edge of the grass, but the step up from the shingle on to the field itself was beyond her capacity, and we succeeded only in burning out the clutch. For the completion of the work, and for the removal of the now useless Land Rover, we had two days later to hire a break-down lorry from a garage twenty miles away. The lorry was able to winch the *Polar Star* on to the grass, but the removal of the reluctant Land Rover presented greater difficulties. At the end of three hours the cortège had progressed less than a hundred yards up the one in three gradient of the track, and it was some seven hours after the beginning of the operation when, after midnight, the exhausted pall-bearers reached the metalled road at Druimfiaclach. It is such frequent incidents as these that render life at Camusfeàrna more costly than that of many a great mansion house nearer to the amenities of civilisation.

All this was after the great freeze-up. First had come tempests and hurricanes that knocked the fences flat, whisked the slates from the roof like leaves in autumn, blew dinghies about as if they were pieces of paper, while the surf fell upon the windows of the house and crusted them thick with salt. The gentle slope of the high sand-dunes to the sea became overnight a vertical cliff some ten feet high as the invading waves roared in and battered the dunes into a resistant wall; the racing torrent of the burn in spate undermined the roots of the alders and the trees fell; the length and breadth of the field, where the bent-grass itself lay flattened by the wind, was scattered with seaweed and flotsam from the beach. It had been impossible to watch the sea, for one could not stand upright without support, much less keep one's eyes open as the hurricane hurled mingled spume and sand landward at a hundred miles an hour.

When the days of tempest were over it began to snow, and – something I had only seen once before at Camusfeàrna – it lay right down to the sea's edge. Slowly it turned intensely cold; the burn froze over and then finally the waterfall itself. It froze solid, still in the form of a waterfall, so that only the lack of movement betrayed its sculptural substance. Giant icicles formed a fringe from the banks of the pool beneath it, icicles more than seven feet long and as thick as a man's arm, and the deep pool itself was solid for more than two feet. The snow fell as though it would never end. Flat on the field and down to the tide it lay nearly two feet deep, and on the margin of the sea itself floated a tinkling crust of ice. On the hill above us the road was blocked; there the snow lay evenly more than a yard deep, and there were drifts into which an elephant could have disappeared.

We had staying with us a Sicilian, Eugenio Vicari, who had never seen snow lie before; months earlier, when his visit had first been planned, I had tried to disabuse him of the image he had built of Camusfeàrna, that of a cottage in deep snow surrounded by Christmas trees. I had told him that it would be wet and windy and dark and that the only snow would be on the hilltops. Now he looked at me and grinned and said: '*Credo che non conosci bene la Scozzia!*'

His arrival at the station thirty-five miles away had produced a moment of fine farce, a linguistic misunderstanding that it would be hard to better. Sitting in the hotel lounge and looking out over the small bleak village, he asked me whether there were any churches in the town. It was a natural enough question, for every Sicilian village is dominated by its church tower, and from where we sat there was no evidence of any ecclesiastical architecture whatsoever in the whole community. The word he used for church was, I thought, '*moschea*', literally a mosque, but used in some parts of Sicily to denote any religious building; a result, no doubt, of the long Arab occupation of the island. I replied that there were, in fact, three, but they were on the outskirts of the town. What, he asked solemnly, were they like? He would find them very different from his own, I said; some of them did not even approve of music or bells, considering such things frivolities. In short, I summed up, he would find them very serious-minded, they might even seem to him to be preoccupied by death and the day of judgement. At this moment he could contain the joke no longer and he exploded. He was so helpless with laughter that it was minutes before I could understand – he had not used the word '*moschea*', but '*mosca*', the plural forms being nearly identical. He had, in fact, asked whether there were no flies in the town. When at the end of his visit he left from the same station he asked me to say good-bye to the three serious minded flies and tell them not to worry so much about the day of judgement.

There was one further equally glorious misunderstanding during his stay, but it is difficult to convey the full nuance without offence. It was New Year's Eve; inside the house the wireless was blaring, the fire blazing, the room hung with Christmas decoration. Outside was the ever-intensifying cold of frozen snow and bare starlit skies. Jimmy had been out, and came back in a high state of excitement. 'The burn's frozen solid!' he announced. 'I've just walked right across it where it's deepest – I jumped up and down and it didn't even creak!' Eugenio, interested by Jimmy's obvious mood of high enthusiasm, asked me to translate. I said: '*Ha camminato sul torrente gelato*' – he walked on the frozen burn. Eugenio looked very puzzled. 'Why?' he asked, with great insistence. 'Why?' This seemed to me unwarrantable obtuseness; but perhaps, I thought, to a Sicilian who had never before seen natural ice there was nothing odd in being able to walk on it at sea-level. I said somewhat testly: 'What do you mean "Why?" It is a very remarkable thing to be able to do, and certainly the first time we've ever been able to do it here.' His astonishment deepened visibly; his forehead was furrowed with the effort to understand. 'Is it a ritual?' he asked, plainly anxious to enter as fully into the curiosities of Scottish life as I had once attempted to be absorbed into peasant Sicily. 'A ritual?' I replied. 'No, it's not a ritual, although in the old days, on big rivers like the Thames these things became almost a ritual – things like roasting an ox whole on the ice of the Thames, or driving a coach and four horses across it. Here, it is just extraordinary to be able to walk across a small frozen river at sea-level – if it happened every year I suppose in time we'd make a ritual of it. Do you understand now?' I saw the same expression creeping into his big dark eyes as when he had begun to comprehend our confusion of issue about flies and churches. He was now obviously controlling a fit of giggles with the greatest difficulty. 'Would you mind,' he asked with painful politeness, 'would you mind repeating what you first said when I asked what Jimmy was so excited about?' I repeated it: '*Ha camminato sul torrente gelato.*' He began to choke with suppressed giggles, then the dam gave way altogether and he was helpless, rolling from side to side, literally crying with laughter. Although I had not yet understood the joke his mood was irresistible, and I began to find myself in the same state. 'What did you think I'd said?' I kept on demanding, but it was minutes before he found enough control to answer me. Then he gasped out: 'I didn't hear the letter "c". I suppose it was the wireless making all that noise – I thought you said "*ha minato sul torrente gelato!*" ' Now *minare* is the Italian slang verb for solitary sexual indulgence. Thus the picture of a strange esoteric ritual had been forming in Eugenio's mind, a ritual more weird, surely, than any of the archaic practices of his country. The year the Thames froze over and Charles II masturbated on the ice. . . .

Everywhere the snow went on falling, but the days were for

the most part bright and sunny and the sea blue, and the plantation of young firs on the hillside above us became a regiment of Christmas trees. We improvised a toboggan, to the huge delight of Teko, who would straddle it to be towed round at ever-increasing speed. He seemed to understand the idea very soon, and when we pulled the toboggan to the top of a slope he would climb on to it and wait with obvious impatience for someone to shove it off down the slope. As it began to slow he would kick with his hind legs to maintain the impetus, and when his chariot finally came to rest he would work angrily at the ropes with his teeth, as if by so doing he could once more coax it into movement. We sent to London for a real toboggan, but by the time it arrived the snow had long gone and had given place to mud and quag-mire.

The geese had left us, the wild grey geese that I had domesticated at Camusfeàrna two and half years before. The day before the snow began they had taken wing, spiralled high above Druim-fiaclach and made off southward at a great height. Of the eleven that left, only three came back in the spring; the rest, no doubt, suffered the common fate of wild creatures that have been taught to trust their worst enemy.

During all this time we had, as I have said, little use from the *Polar Star*, yet one glorious morning will always stand out in my memory. Since the roads were still blocked by snow when the time came for Eugenio to return to Sicily, we could only reach the distant station by sea. The winter sun was just up in a bare blue sky, the shadows still long and blue upon the snow, and the great white hills all about us were salmon-pink above a smooth enamel sea of beetle-wing blue. On every side so little showed through the snow that the only colours of which one was aware were those of its varying tones, from shadows to sunlit brilliance, and the two blues of sea and sky. The *Polar Star* roared north between the frozen mountains, and her great leaping seething wake held the reflected light of the sun and the snows; to us on board her the racing boat seemed the only moving thing in a world of ice-cold colour, her speed the direct expression of human exhilaration.

In February 1962 Malcolm and Paula Macdonald, who had given Edal to me in the spring of 1959, came to Camusfeàrna to visit her after an absence of nearly three years. I had told them of all that had happened during the past six months, of her attack upon Terry and of her apparent hatred of women, and they both agreed that it would be inadvisable for Paula to meet Edal face to face. Malcolm would go into her room with Jimmy, and Paula would watch over the waist-high partition that separated Jimmy's sitting-room from Edal's quarters. We were in the living-room when we reached this sensible decision, and a moment or two later I was called to the telephone to take a long-distance call. The telephone conversation was prolonged, and it was some quarter of an hour later that I returned, to find the living-room empty. I went across to Jimmy's house, and as I entered his sitting-room I at first saw nobody. Then I heard voices from beyond Edal's partition, and hurried forward. Sitting on the bed were Jimmy, Malcolm and Paula, and to the last two Edal was making every demonstration of the profoundest welcome and affection. It might have been thought surprising that Edal should remember them at all after that long lapse of time and the mental and physical crises through which she had passed; this, however, was not a question of mere recognition but of positive joy. She squirmed and beamed and pushed her fingers into their mouths; then, as Paula talked to Edal the baby language to which she had been accustomed as an infant, Edal reverted to behaviour that she had not displayed for a full two years. When Paula had first brought her to Camusfeàrna Edal had a well-established and slightly inconvenient method of displaying her affection for her foster-parent, that of sucking and nibbling at Paula's neck. This she had reserved for Paula only, and had never transferred the pattern to Jimmy or myself; now she climbed up on Paula's lap and went into her old ritual as though it were days rather than years that Paula had been away.

It was, in some respects, a heart-rending reunion, for some six weeks before, the two West African otter cubs that Malcolm and Paula had brought back from Nigeria to replace Edal had been killed. These two were without exception the most domesticated

128

and endearing otters I had ever seen, living totally free and be-
having like very well brought-up but extremely playful dogs. A
minister of the Church of Scotland, mooching along the fore-
shore with a shot gun, found them at play by the tide's edge and
shot them. One was killed outright, the other died of her wounds
in the water. The Lord gave man control over the beasts of the
field, as this minister reminded a journalist.

In the course of that winter of 1961–62 we fortuitously acquired
two more otters, and once again with the element of coincidence
that would seem by now to have become a stereotype. First, a
gamekeeper telephoned from the south of Scotland. That afternoon, he told me, he had been walking along a river bank when
he had come unexpectedly upon a bitch otter with four very
small cubs; one had been farther ashore than the others and found
his route to the river blocked by a man and a dog. He just
squatted and blinked, as though considering at leisure the correct
course of action in these totally unfamiliar circumstances.
Probably it was this certain gormlessness of personality which
has to some extent characterised his existence ever since, that
saved his life – for the gamekeeper, seeing this very small creature
just sitting there and blinking hopelessly at him, threw a game-
bag over it and picked it up. He took it home, put it in a box
with some wire-netting over the top, and telephoned to me.
    Despite the complications of the existing otter *ménage* at
Camusfeàrna, I did not hesitate. I had always wanted a British
otter, and had come near to realising this ambition when in a
previous summer a local keeper had brought me a small female
cub that his terriers had caught, but alas she proved to have a
double compound fracture of the lower jaw, and were it to remain
unset she would for all her life have been unable to feed herself.
Jimmy and I bottle-fed her and tended her wound for a few
weeks, but when at last the necessary surgery was carried out in a
distant town she died of post-operational shock. Now this
completely undamaged cub was more than I could resist.
    Transport, however, presented problems. As nobody knew
whether or not the cub was weaned it clearly could not be sent

unaccompanied on a long train journey; Jimmy was on holiday in the south, Terry was not yet old enough to drive a car, and I could not leave him in sole charge at Camusfeàrna. I hired a driver and my neighbour, Mary Mackinnon, volunteered to make the three hundred mile journey in my Land Rover.

When two days later I went up the hill to Druimfiaclach to meet them I carried on my back a wicker fishing creel, thinking this to be an ideal container for a small and possibly very active creature intent upon escape. This picture, however, proved entirely false. When I entered the kitchen at Druimfiaclach, Mary was sitting with the cub on her knee, and it looked remarkably domesticated if not particularly intelligent. I carried it down to Camusfeàrna inside my shirt, and it fed contentedly from a bottle immediately after arrival.

A few weeks later, after I had gone to London to be married, another unweaned cub arrived. The first had been a male, the second, to dot the i's of the coincidence, was a female. Jimmy received a telephone call from the Isle of Skye, to say that a bitch otter in milk had been shot a few days before and now a road-mender had found a tiny unweaned female cub in a ditch. Within three days the two were together in the upstairs room that Edal used to occupy.

The male we had named Mossy, after the earlier cub that died; the female was christened in my absence by the day of her arrival, Monday. How the characters of each of these two would have developed in the absence of the other, it is impossible to say. Mossy, certainly, would have demanded a great deal of patience. As long as he was kept in a large box and only lifted from it to take his bottle he appeared docile and promising, but when he was liberated in the room he did not display the confidence I had expected. I had to sleep on a mattress on the floor before he would consent to curl up in the crook of my knee as all my other otters had liked to do, and he would avoid being handled if he could. It took a fortnight of patience before he would allow us to begin to handle him again and before he started to play with such moving objects as a screwed-up ball of paper on the end of a string. Perhaps he would have developed into a truly dog-like creature had I not had to go south to London and had Monday not arrived a few days later, but I fancy that his I.Q. would always have remained noticeably low.

Monday, by contrast, was from the beginning utterly confident and of a very high degree of intelligence. She was visibly the younger of the two, being little larger than a big rat when she arrived. At the start Jimmy kept her separate from Mossy; she lived in a large basket by the kitchen fire, and if she had remained alone there can be no doubt that she would have become an apotheosis among domesticated otters. When, however, after a few days, she climbed from her basket, explored her new surroundings, and fell wolfishly upon a plate of roast mutton, Jimmy decided that the time had come to introduce her to her future mate.

Carried upstairs to Mossy's room she at first stayed quite still, while Mossy advanced and withdrew from her again and again. At last she followed him, a little uncertainly, as he moved away from her, and from that moment he took possession of her. He nuzzled her and climbed all over her, making a small, high wickering sound in the back of his throat, and when Jimmy went to pick her up Mossy made an angry dart at him with the explosive breathing noise in the cheeks that is his sound of aggression.

Every day Monday spent a little time in that room, before being returned to the kitchen, and each day Mossy became more possessive and more angry when she was removed. In less than a week she took up permanent quarters with him, and from then on Mossy took no interest in human beings except as purveyors of eel meat. Though Monday remained confiding, the two were self-sufficient. They indulged in endless mutual grooming, though in this as in all else Monday remained the subservient partner and Mossy retained his demanding male arrogance. A typical and oft-repeated tableau was that of Mossy lying at ease upon his back, preening, in a desultory way, his chest and forearms, while at the lower end of his body Monday performed for him services that afforded him the greatest evident delight. They slept much throughout the day, showing a preference for darkness; sometimes they would curl up together underneath a chest of drawers, but more often they appeared as a conspicuous and faintly stirring lump under the carpet. Towards evening they would awake and begin to play games that gathered tempo until from the living-room the noise above resembled nothing so much as a couple of toy trains running on the rimless spokes of their wheels. Round and round the bare boarding next to the walls they would race tirelessly, the thunder of their progress interrupted only by Mossy's inevitable catching of Monday, when the sounds of galloping feet would change to prolonged and concerted wickering. This wickering is extremely difficult to describe; it is a very rapidly repeated staccato but musical note of which the effect is almost of something mechanical. It is in the treble key; perhaps the nearest parallel would be the concept of a motor-mower whose voice had not yet broken, and the nearest approach to accurate reproduction is to rub a wetted finger-tip quickly to and fro over half an inch of glass surface.

Humans, in their role of providers, remained creatures of enormous importance to Mossy and Monday, and at the sound of a step on the stairway they would make a single competitive rush for the half-door that separated them from the landing. After the first few weeks we had removed the carpet until such time as outdoor quarters could be arranged for Mossy and Monday, so that by now there was nothing to deaden the patter, or thunder, of their tiny feet on bare linoleum. We tape-recorded the noise of this race from one corner of the room to that diagonally opposite, and the effect is that of a sound-track deliberately speeded up, so that it becomes simply a solid roar, without perceptible impact of individual feet. At the end one can distinguish one single tap on the drum, so to speak – the sound of their forepaws hitting the door as they stood up against it in frenzied anticipation.

Sometimes Dirk the deerhound would accompany whoever went up to feed them; he would put his paws up on the half-door and gaze down with benign interest at the sharp little faces looking up at his.

At this time we fed Mossy and Monday by hand upon pieces of chopped eel, partly so that they could thus be forced daily into

Agadir
Right – Moulay Ahmed El Alaoui, King Mohammed V of Morocco, and Crown Prince Hassan

Children of Agadir

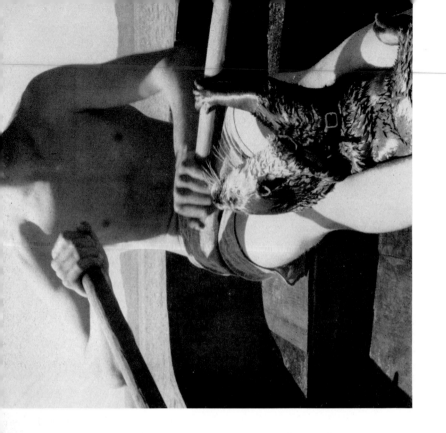

Teko soon after his arrival at Camusfeàrna

Terry and the Greylag geese on Camusfeàrna beach

Teko at play

'In bright oases of the desert South'

Edal in her new quarters

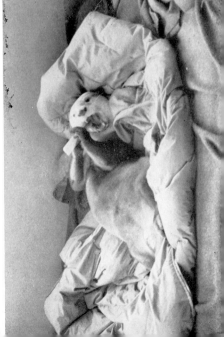

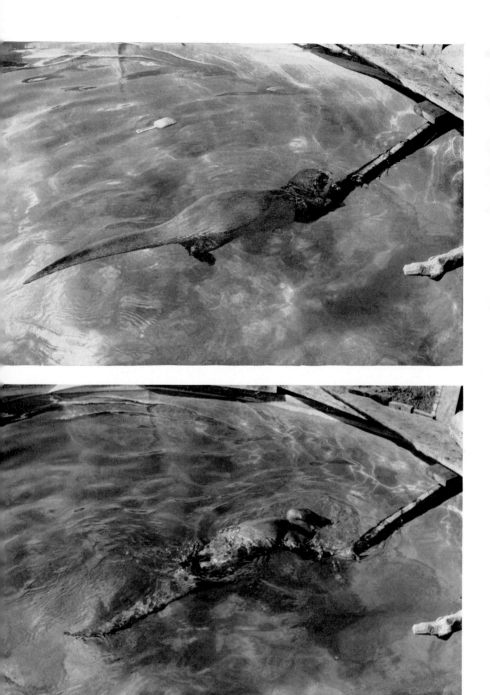

Edal exploring the syphon outflow to her new pool

Left – Teko and Dirk   *Above* – Teko by his new pool

Teko's reaction to a life-belt was to eat it

Teko demonstrates the use of his fingers while playing with a net float

Beaching the *Polar Star*

Camusfeàrna, winter 1961–62

The frozen waterfall

Reunion between Edal and her original foster parents –
Jimmy, Edal, Malcolm and Paula Macdonald

Mossy as an infant

Mossy during the first weeks

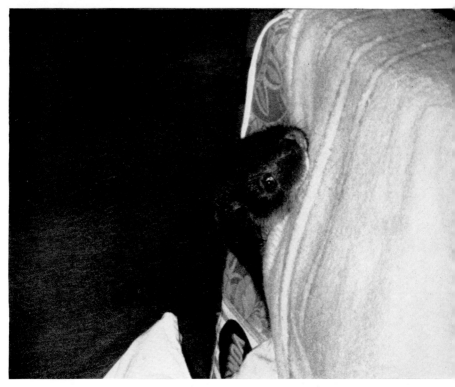

Terry and Monday
on the day she
arrived

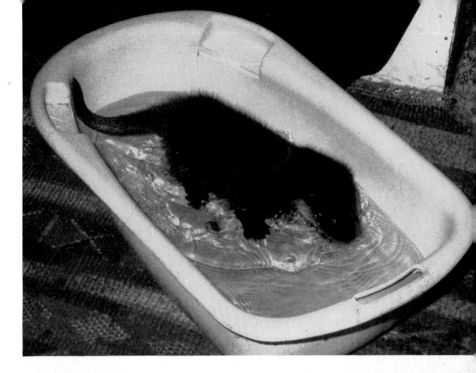

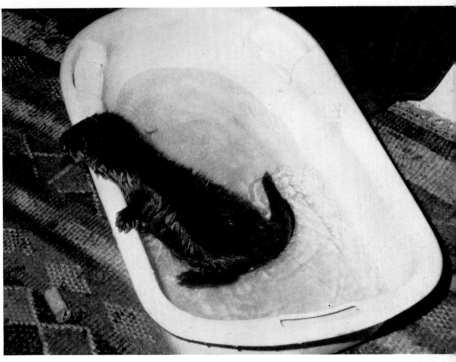

Monday's first experiments in water

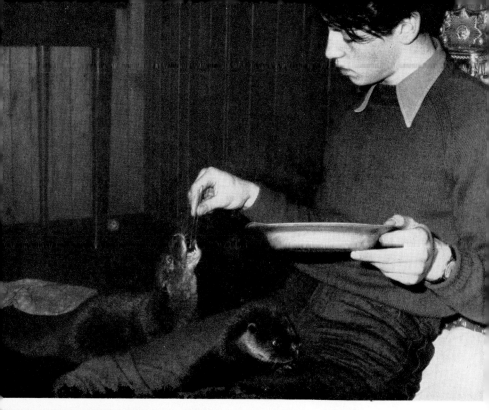

Mossy and
Monday. 'In less
than a week she
took up perma-
nent quarters with
him.'

human contact and so retain some domesticity, but partly, also, in order to ensure that each received a due share; for Mossy, despite his possessiveness towards his consort, had proved himself an apostle of enlightened self-interest, and ungallant to the ultimate degree. Anything he could possibly snatch from her he did, and when we had first offered them whole eels he had contrived to carry the whole lot, in one journey to a distant corner, where while eating the first he snarlingly guarded the remainder. If during this display of anti-feminism one gave another eel to Monday, he would shoot across the room from his corner, whisk it away from her, and add it to his own defended store. There was no solution but to feed each with inch-long lengths of eel from a pair of tweezers; these were necessary because, while Monday took these bonbons with all the gentleness of a well-trained dog, Mossy was by instinct a grabber, and cared nothing whether or not his needle-sharp teeth enclosed more than a piece of eel. At the time I resented Mossy, and thought only what a rewarding animal to domesticate Monday would have been without him, for it was not until some three months later that we moved them outside and had all the unwearying joy of watching two wild otters at play in a glass tank.

Meanwhile both these otters had to receive the injections necessary to ensure their future health. The injections were in two doses at a fortnight's interval, and in this matter, too, Monday displayed most strikingly the quality of intelligence that Mossy lacked. Neither of them was handleable in the sense that they could be held still while being injected with a hypodermic needle; but to this problem the same resourceful vet, Donald MacLennan, who had saved Edal's life, had as always brought answers. He introduced us to an instrument I had never seen, a dog-catcher; a long metal tube from the distal end of which protrudes a noose that can be drawn tight from the butt. Neither animal being familiar with the function or potentialities of this device, the first injections produced no difficulty at all, and the work was completed in five minutes. We began with Monday, because she was the first to go into a corner where she could be walled off and confined by a piece of boarding some three feet high and four feet long. After that initial mistake on her part, she displayed, however, a cunning in avoiding the noose that no human brain in the same body could possibly have surpassed. She had, after all, only her jaws and her two forepaws at her disposal, for after the first quarter of an hour we had closed her in so completely that she had no room to manoeuvre. Again and again as the noose descended towards her head she would anticipate trouble by going to meet it – she would spring up and seize it between her teeth, worry it, and throw it back over her shoulder with a flick of the neck. More than once, when someone had momentarily succeeded in distracting her attention and we had the noose almost in position, she would get her paws inside it and pull it open with that extraordinary strength which even very small otters can display. It took three-quarters of an hour, and the cooperation of three people, before we finally secured her; it had been a hateful proceeding, and I dreaded its repetition with Mossy.

I need not have worried. While Monday had clearly retained an acute recollection of the noose – almost, one is tempted to write, an understanding of its mechanical principle – that great booby Mossy, although angry and blustering at being boarded off into a narrow corner of the room, had no more idea of how to avoid capture than he had shown on the river bank in his extreme infancy. With him it was all over in three minutes.

For both of them, in however varying degree, I felt that the experience must have been traumatic, and I expected that it would be a long time before they recovered their trust in us, even as providers of food. I thought it would be weeks before we again heard that rush of scampering feet at the sound of a boot on the stair. In fact it was less than an hour; neither seemed to bear us any ill-will for the outrages we had committed upon their persons.

They were, however, rapidly growing up, and both our own pressure upon the limited accommodation of the house and their increasing agility made it necessary to move them to outdoor quarters. It was, perhaps, the second factor that forced the decision upon us, for one incident made it evident that we could no longer ventilate the room by leaving the top of the window open without running the risk of their exit. We had removed a top drawer from the chest of drawers in order to sort through its contents, and immediately Mossy and Monday saw the resulting dark cavern as an ideal retreat from unwelcome human visitors. That this new den was some four feet from the ground troubled them not at all; the exact process by which they progressed from the floor to invisibility was too quick for the eye to follow, but the fact remained that the vertical distance was greater than that which they would have to ascend to reach the window. We made somewhat hasty preparations for their removal to an enclosure immediately outside the living-room window. From then on they became Lavinia's special care, and it is better that she rather than I should write the next chapter of their history.

'When I became engaged to Gavin in November 1961, it was inevitable that I was asked by a great many different people a great number of questions such as: "How will you like living a great deal of the time at a place as remote as Camusfeàrna?" "Do you like the otters and get on with them?", etc. All these questions I answered in the affirmative because in marrying, a woman consciously takes on not only the man, but also the pattern of his life and whatever it contains. For me, this pattern was in theory entirely acceptable but the reality only began after we returned from our stay in North Africa following our marriage, when the real work began of fitting into a long-established bachelor establishment, of putting down my own roots in my new home. I was a new girl, and above me in seniority of time were Gavin, Jimmy, Terry – and Edal and Teko. The difficulty here was that in a *ménage* in which otter and human lives were inextricably woven, I found that, whereas I had complete contact with the humans, I could, by virtue of being a stranger and a woman, only have the remotest contact with the otters; nothing more than talking to them over a dividing fence as I went to and fro during the course of the day; or at most sometimes throwing their food to them and thereby establishing that I was friend and not foe, even though a somewhat distant and negative one.

'It was not until the two babies, Mossy and Monday, were

moved out into their enclosure, that I suddenly realised that I was not after all the only new girl. They had, in fact, come to Camusfeàrna at exactly the same moment as I had, and all three of us were busy settling in in our various ways. The realisation of this made me view them in a completely new light, and I began to see them not as just two more of these strange, fascinating but remote creatures of whom I had no experience and with whom I had no personal contact, but as two highly individual animals with their own distinct personalities; animals with whom I could, given time and patience, establish a much more rewarding relationship than that of a mere interested and appreciative onlooker.

'When we returned to Camusfeàrna in the late spring, Mossy and Monday were still in their winter quarters in one of the upstairs rooms, the only home, in fact, that they had known since they were tiny cubs and had first come to us. They were shy, timid creatures, made more so by the facts of their mutual companionship, and that none of us had been able to give them enough of our time to accustom them completely to close human contact. Then came the day when their new outside enclosure was ready for them; their house was built and their blanket put on the sleeping-perch inside it; the glass water-tank, dismantled from Gavin's London house and brought up by me in the Land Rover, had been reassembled (but not yet filled); their empty giant tortoise shell in which they played hide-and-seek for hours on end had been carried down and put on the grass; and finally, Gavin and Terry had by some superhuman effort of strength and incredible precision managed to roll an enormous old tree stump through the gate, making both a decorative feature in the enclosure, and a practical stepping-stone for them in and out of the tank. While Gavin and Terry were resting, panting from their exertions, I followed with handfuls of earth and clumps of sea pinks, hoping they would take root in the crevices of the wood; but when eventually the two little otters discovered the fun of scrambling all over the stump, the garden we had so quickly created for them disappeared with equal rapidity. The moment finally came to move Mossy and Monday themselves – a manoeuvre which was accomplished with far greater ease and speed than any of us had dared hoped for. They were lured into a forty-gallon oil drum placed on its side; this apparently held no terrors for them, for after a very short time they nosed their way inside with true otter inquisitiveness, and someone standing behind was able to fold down the cut lid and turn the oil drum upright. The bunghole in the side we left open and all the way down the staircase and out to their new home, they were jostling for a place at this window and looking out with their bright beady eyes at the unfamiliar world beyond their bedroom door. Once inside the enclosure, we laid the drum on its side once more and stood back to watch them slowly and cautiously emerging. It was a bright, sunny day, and this added to their confusion, for their eyes were totally unaccustomed to anything but the subdued light of the pine-panelled room in which they had spent their earliest months. However, the warmth of that day and those following was on the whole fortunate, for the temperature change from indoor to outdoor life was not too abrupt for them.

'We watched them nosing their way blindly round their strange new surroundings, passing by their familiar tortoise shell with not so much as a flicker of pleased recognition, and finally finding the open door to their house, they bolted inside, into the darkest corner beneath the sleeping-perch. That was the last we saw of them for many days, but for their brief and timid sorties in the late evening in search of food which they grabbed and carried back at once to the safety of their house. We knew they emerged sometimes in the darkness of the night because from inside the house we occasionally heard little squeals and nickering noises, but at the slightest sound of human footsteps they would bolt back to their hideout.

'It was at this point in their lives that I found myself becoming more and more absorbed by the thought of these two tiny bewildered creatures who remained so obstinately out of sight; how they could be lured out and given the confidence to remain out in daylight without this precipitate flight at the first sound of clumping boots. We did attempt one day to break them of their nocturnal habit by closing their door behind them when they had emerged to find food, but they looked so pathetically miserable, huddled together in the shaded right-angle of their house and the fence, that we very quickly relented and reopened the door for them to return to the reassuring darkness of their home. But as the days went by and there was little noticeable improvement in this situation, we began to fear that they would remain as creatures of nocturnal habit.

'At this point, in early June, I had to go down to London for about ten days, and whilst I was away, Gavin tried new tactics by changing their feeding times. They had been having breakfast-eels at the same time as Edal and Teko had theirs, but that meant that no sooner had Mossy and Monday grabbed their ration, than they disappeared straight back into their house, and were not seen again until in the late evening the need of more food forced them to emerge once more. By postponing their morning feeding time we achieved exactly what we hoped for; they now ventured out and nosed their way round the enclosure with steadily increasing confidence and curiosity, simply through the dictates of their stomachs. Moreover, this enforced waiting period even began to awaken their enthusiasm for any passing human who they thought might be the bearer of their eagerly awaited eels.

'When I travelled up again, Gavin was already on his way down as he had to be in London on business for a few days. We broke our journeys for a couple of days at a mutual rendezvous, and then continued our separate ways north and south. When I got back to Camusfeàrna, I took over where he had left off in trying to win the confidence of the baby otters. It was entirely fascinating, especially as for me the attempt to establish contact with otters was a completely new experience. Although to the trained eye Mossy and Monday were easily indentifiable, to begin with I found myself getting very muddled and mistaking him for her, and vice versa – unless of course they were both in view, when the difference in size was obvious. We had all of us also adopted a sort of sing-song call to them, joining their names together, so there was no question of each coming to their own name at that stage. (Later, when feeding them by hand, I always made a point of talking to them each individually, and by name.) Now I began to see very clearly not only the physical difference, but also how unalike they were in character. Mossy, always the larger of the two, was by far the less intelligent and had a definitely boorish streak both in his treatment of Monday and of humans. His manners are, on the whole, appalling; he is a grabber by nature, and his ungentlemanly conduct towards Monday together with the expression on his face, altogether broader and flatter than hers, earned him the nickname of Reggie, after one of Evelyn Waugh's more oafish characters.

'Whereas Mossy's personality remains consistently dull – and thereby very often comic – Monday's by contrast is brilliant, gay and quick-witted. Her small, pointed face is always alive with curiosity and silent laughter, and she very quickly became the leader in all enterprise, though her devotion to her slow and unenterprising companion never wavered. Invariably, when food was thrown to them over the fence, it was Mossy who grabbed the first eel with a furious warning squeal at her, and one could almost see her shrug her shoulder as she waited, unmoved, for the next one. Sometimes he went too far with her and tried to take an eel from her, but at this a quick nip, a well-timed warning to watch his manners, would send him flying.

'We had a lot of trouble with the glass water-tank which we had hoped to have filled by the time the otters were in their new enclosure. One of the sheets of glass, of which there were three on each side and one at either end, had cracked when we first filled the tank, and we had to wait some days for a replacement. In the meantime we put the old hip-bath on the grass, but it was so shallow that after a few minutes of Mossy's and Monday's vigorous splashing nothing remained but an inch or two of almost pure mud, and the ground around it became more and more like a soggy ploughed field. But from their obvious enjoyment of it, it was plain that they would spend far more time out of doors when they had a permanent pool; we waited with growing impatience for the arrival of the new piece of glass, and then for the cement to dry and harden before we could again fill the tank with water. This was finally accomplished, but it was now late

June, the time unfortunately which Gavin had to spend in London. Terry was also away on holiday so only Jimmy and I witnessed the great event of their introduction to deep water.

'Before describing this, I should explain that the tank had been set up directly in front of the living-room window; across this window with its back to the light is a sofa, and by kneeling on it we had a perfect view of the tank. It was in that position that Jimmy and I spent many hours during the next few days. The tank itself measured approximately eight feet long by three feet wide by three feet deep, the glass panels held together by an iron frame, giving it an all-round rim of about three inches wide, and two surface cross-bars. We knew that entering the tank presented no problem to the otters; they could either go via the tree-stump, or simply by jumping straight from the ground on to the rim. This they had in fact been doing with the greatest of ease when the tank was empty, balancing their way along it and the cross-bars. Now, with the tank filled to the brim with clear water, we waited by the window in the long evening light and watched for the reward of our work.

'As was their wont at that time, they emerged from their house about sundown, when the bustle of the day was over and the light had begun to fade. They had a small doorway at the furthest corner of their house, just where it formed a right-angle against the fence; from this they would creep out slowly and cautiously, with wary glances all round as they advanced, and at the slightest noise would dive back to security. Later, as their confidence increased and with it their acceptance of the house-hold, they watched everything with interest – footsteps still brought them clamouring to the wire-netting in the hope that every passing friend was a bringer of food, but if the footsteps were those of a stranger they would vanish immediately.

'On this particular evening, they explored the way step by step, and finally reached the tank. When they leapt up on to the rim and found not empty space but cold clear water, their astonish-ment was enormous, and their balance nearly upset. From this point their two separate personalities emerged even more clearly than before – Mossy the backward boy, Monday the forward girl. She dipped her nose in the water, and then again, deeper, shaking the drops from her face each time she withdrew her head, but each time plunging it a little further down until finally the inevitable happened; she lost her balance and fell in. With a twist of remarkable agility she was already holding on to the edge with her hands, as I clutched Jimmy's coat sleeve with anxiety and muttered "Are you sure she will be all right, Jimmy? Are you *sure* she will know how to swim?" However, she hauled herself out on to the rim with ease and then repeated the whole manoeuvre, but now deliberately and with obvious relish and greater daring each time. For quite a while she splashed in and out, but always she clung to the edge with her hands. Every now and then she would leap down to terra firma, where Mossy was moving about in a puzzled, aimless manner. She seemed to be both teasing him for his timidity, and yet encouraging him to be brave and join her in this delicious new game, but the most he could achieve was an occasional cautious prowl along the edge.

'Quite suddenly she was in and somehow out of sight; I found myself holding my breath, as one does when watching a swimmer who has dived. Unlike a human swimmer, however, she did not reappear, and with an awful sensation of choking I burst out: "Jimmy, *quick*! She's stuck." Jimmy shot out of the door, and at the unexpected interruption Monday shot out of the tank and bolted into her house.

'We watched her until it was too dark to see out of the window any more, and it was the most wonderful spectacle of under-water *joie-de-vivre* I have ever seen. After that initial plunge she appeared to have every movement, every trick of swimming, at her finger-tips; she had grace, and speed and beauty – a water ballerina. She was totally absorbed and had completely forgotten the luckless Mossy, who was still no further than the stage of dipping his big toe in at the water's edge. Jimmy and I finally turned away from the window and nibbled at our long-forgotten supper, but we could hear the splashing in the tank for the rest of the evening, and perhaps Monday swam all night long, for she was still at it when I fell asleep.

'The advent of water brought about completely the change we

141

had hoped for in the habits of Mossy and Monday, and eventually they were as content by day as by night in their routine of swimming, eating and sleeping. But before this happened Jimmy and I had two more days of watching before Mossy mastered the art of swimming – two days in which he clung to the side, somersaulted over the cross-bars, kicked with his hind legs, thrashed with his tail; he would lose his balance and go in head-first and still manage to keep a grip on the side with his back toes. It was very funny and very clownish; but he would not, could not bring himself to let go. Monday mocked and teased him mercilessly, darting and diving below and around him, nipping at his tail and his toes. Finally she simply gave him a great shove and it was all over – to his patent surprise he suddenly discovered that he could swim. They began to evolve endless and intricate games together – water-ballets, which started in slow motion and worked up gradually to a long crescendo of movement, until the tank seemed a rapidly boiling cauldron and the two gyrating animals appeared to be twenty. Hide-and-seek, wrestling, boxing, "pat-a-cake" with hands or noses – in and out the tank, on to the tree stump, down the other side, hide under the tortoise shell. We have dawdled away many minutes watching their play.

'Gavin returned home a few days later and was delighted by the change he found. Now that the babies were so much less shy, he and Jimmy could hope to obtain some photographs or films of their underwater aquabatics whenever weather and light conditions allowed. We still referred to them as "the babies" but in fact they were growing fast, looking supremely healthy, and appeared to have insatiable appetites. At this stage they were supposed to receive four eels each for breakfast, the same in the afternoon, and a further two or three in the evening. But on going out at about ten or eleven at night, one would invariably hear a rush of tiny feet and see two small figures standing upright, side by side, holding on to the wire-netting and demanding more to eat. So we introduced a fourth feeding time; but Mossy and Monday were great believers in the theory that there is no harm in asking, and having many times received this extra meal from the hands of one of us they would pretend to the next passer-by that it had been forgotten.

'I was delighted with the change in their daily routine, for I wanted them to be much tamer than they were at present, and there was clearly very little hope of achieving this while they persisted in hiding by day. Now, however, Monday (in the lead as usual) began to come out when I called, with Mossy trailing behind suspiciously. I began to go into the enclosure with ready chopped-up eels, to draw out hand-feeding them for as long as possible. It was tremendously rewarding, and I found myself looking forward to feeding-times just as much as the otters clearly did – for our different reasons. Again, at this exercise, their two natures showed up markedly according to the now familiar pattern; I adopted a sitting position from the start, squatting back on my heels, and very quickly Monday came right up on to my lap to take her piece of eel. She was always absolutely gentle and delicate in her movements, and we have often thought that but for her strong bond with Mossy she could have become a complete household pet. He, as was to be expected, made a terrible fuss when being hand-fed; he took it all right, but with a lunge and a snatch, accompanied by furious squeals. I have often expected to see a small chunk of my finger or thumb go with the piece of eel; but quite suddenly and to my surprise and delight he also grew gentle. But this may not have been so much a triumph of taming on my part as a result or example of good behaviour from Monday.

'Their attitude to other animals was curiously matter-of-fact – far more so than to humans, with whom, as I have already said, they were extremely shy but for the recognised members of the household. Dirk the deerhound has always been a source of interest to them, and I have often watched long, snuffly conversations going on through the wire, the otters on their hind legs raising their small button noses to meet the dog's large wet one. But the funniest encounter occurred one day in the autumn between Monday and one of the greylag geese. I was in the otters' enclosure doing something or other by the tank, and caught sight of the geese stalking by the open gate in single file like slow, self-important sentries. The last one decided to turn in down the path to the front door, and at the same moment Monday came out of the side door of her house. They caught sight of each other simultaneously; the goose became quite hysterical, either with rage or fear, or possibly both, and danced up and down with wings extended, hissing loudly. Monday was by this time on her hind legs holding on to the wire with one hand, and a comical expression of mild surprise and interest on her face. I called as loudly as I dared to Gavin, who was working in his room to bring a camera quickly before the scene dissolved; it was one of the occasions so frequent at Camusfeàrna, when I have wished that I carried a ciné-camera permanently slung round my neck.'

This was the autumn; both Lavinia and I were abroad during the early winter months, and we did not see Mossy and Monday again until the New Year of 1963.

Conventional insurance policies cover accident, fire and flood, and in a year of miscellaneous mishaps which included the first and last of these items it would perhaps have been unreasonable to expect fire not to have been attracted to Camusfeàrna by its general aura of crisis and vulnerability. I was, of course, alone in the house when it happened. I had been rendering down a great quantity of beef fat; when I had finished I placed the very large basin of liquid fat on the kitchen floor, put a frying pan of water on the electric hotplate with the intention of cooking myself some kippers, and then went to answer the telephone. The conversation lasted some ten minutes; I had a mental eye on the frying pan of water, but I did not think that, starting from cold, it could have evaporated in that time.

Exactly as I put the receiver down there was a muffled but heavy explosion from the kitchen, heavy enough to send a shiver through the pine-panelling of the whole ground-floor. Tearing through into the living-room I looked aghast at the entrance to the small kitchen – the whole doorway was blotted out in a roaring mass of flames whose tongues were even now shooting along the living-room rafters and devouring small pendant objects in their progress. Just inside the main door of the house was a large new fire-extinguisher; with this knowledge I felt quietly confident. I seized this impressive weapon rapidly, carried out the simple instructions printed upon it, advanced as near to the flames as the heat allowed me, and directed the nozzle toward the kitchen ceiling, for this, I thought, was the point from which the flames might take over the rest of the house.

The jet of extinguishing fluid lasted for something less than three seconds; then this pretentiously aggressive and brightly coloured instrument just began to dribble on to the floor. The only tap in the house lay beyond the wall of flames and the nearest water out of doors was Teko's pool. I grabbed two buckets and raced for it; the bolt on his gate was stuck, and when I finally forced it open Teko was waiting to slip past me. By the time I had the two buckets full and the gate closed behind me I thought there was little chance of saving the house; for it is entirely lined with the ideal tinder of Oregon pine-panelling, and I was already considering what should be salvaged and how two irreconcilable otters might be rescued simultaneously with Mossy and Monday, whose room would be the first to go. The first buckets had little effect beyond a blinding cloud of steam; eight times I ran to and fro between the pool and the kitchen, throwing the water to the ceiling in cupped hands, and eight times Teko did all that he knew to make ingress or egress from his enclosure impossible. After the last of these nightmare journeys, I was amazed to see that no flame remained; the walls and ceiling of the kitchen, which had been repainted a week before, were blackened and charred, but no living spark was left.

The first thing to catch my eye among the dismal debris was the remains of something that looked like the casing of a small home-made bomb, the ragged strips of thin, twisted metal that result from an explosion within a container. There were a considerable number of these scattered round the room, and then quite suddenly I saw their origin. Embedded in the basin of fat, now congealed by many gallons of water, was the warhead – the upper half of a deodorant spray of popular make. This tin, evidently, had stood too close to the hotplate on which I had prepared to cook my kippers; it had exploded, and with awful accuracy of aim the upper portion had travelled eight feet to slam into the basin of liquid fat. The force of the impact had sprayed fat all over the walls and ceiling; enough had fallen on the hot plate to start the fire, and this had in turn detonated two more deodorant cans, several pieces of which had also found their way into the fat and given fresh impetus to the flames.

Accident, fire and flood. Not long after the fire came the plague of rats. We had known for some months that for the first time in the history of Camusfeàrna there were a few in the house, but they did not appear to multiply, and caused us little trouble. Now there was a sudden population explosion and, far from our being able to ignore the rats, they became our major preoccupation. Whether they really numbered thousands I do not know, but certainly they gave that impression. Sleep became impossible at night as behind the panelling, they fought and mated, played and ran races, rolling, it seemed, some kind of resonant ball at high speed and for hours on end; food disappeared from the most inaccessible places, and floors and furniture became foul with rat dung; they gnawed through the panelling to allow themselves multiple entry to every room and chewed the upholstery of soft furniture in order to build themselves nests; and, worst outrage of them all, one of their number bit my head twice during one night. Possibly he too was in search of nesting material. To add to their other nauseous characteristics, they were cannibals by apparent preference, for if one of their number were caught in a trap he was invariably eaten before morning.

At first I was unwilling to use rat poison, for the memory of an experience long ago remained fresh in my mind. When I was an undergraduate at Oxford there was a small enclosure in the park containing ornamental waterfowl such as Mandarin and Carolina ducks and a few comparative rarities; every year these birds laid eggs and every year they were eaten by rats, insolently and in daylight before spectators. Waterfowl were in those days one of my major interests and I felt this to be a waste. The park keeper gave me permission to exterminate the rats and, full of youthful enthusiasm, I bought a packet of widely advertised and well known rat poison. On this packet were printed the words 'harmless to poultry and all domestic livestock'. I put poisoned bread and bran in the waterfowl enclosure, and the next morning every single bird in it was dead.

So at the beginning we tried every method of destruction other than poison. Outside, where we had refuse pits among the sand-dunes they had formed a honeycomb of interconnecting burrows having their entrances many yards apart; into these we poured large quantities of petrol and ignited it to form a heavy subterranean detonation. This certainly did kill a great number of rats, but the birth rate evidently remained consistently higher than the death rate. We shot them with shotguns, rifles and pistols; we swiped at them with pokers, sticks and axes; we set for them snares and snap-traps and live-traps, but nothing made any impression upon their numbers.

The very first rat that we caught was in a live-trap on the living-room floor. None of us wanted the task of drowning it, and eventually it was left to me to carry the cage down to the stream. I submerged it immediately; the rat went on running round the cage as if it were in air and not water. No bubbles rose. After perhaps half a minute it put its paws up between the wire mesh of the trap and hung there, looking at me. It went on looking at me; it must have been a further minute or more before I realised that it was dead.

The live-traps were useless. The following day one trap held seven half-grown rats, and the day after there were another six; then no rat ever entered them again. By October the situation was unbearable and we consulted what the ungenteel used to call a rat-catcher, but is in fact a Rodent Operative.

There appeared to me to be only one possible poison, on grounds of safety, efficiency, and humanity, and even this, *Warfarin*, could not completely be guaranteed harmless to the otters. The risk, however, was comparatively small, and in the event our judgement was wholly vindicated, for at the end of a week the otters were in excellent health and there was not a single remaining rat at Camusfeàrna.

In the course of the Rodent Operative's visit I learned much about rats that was strange to me. The common man, he said, tended to think of them as creatures of barnyard and building, in constant association with man; this was wholly fallacious and he would guarantee to find me rats on the pinnacles of the Cuillin Hills. As an example he cited the meteorological station on the summit of Ben Nevis; rats had arrived within a day or two of completion of the hutments, and it would be unreasonable to assume them to have climbed 4,000 feet from the rich refuses of Fort William. It was due to the perpetually wandering habits of the rat, he explained, that they had settled at Camusfeàrna; not a square yard of countryside was unvisited by some rats in the course of six months, and they would stop wherever they found food plentiful. An open refuse-pit, which at Camusfeàrna was our only means of disposing of kitchen rubbish, was irresistible.

He also told me that I had been using the snap-traps, which were simply a larger version of the ordinary mousetrap, in a completely mistaken way. In my innocence I had asked him the best bait to use on these. 'None,' he replied. 'You don't bait them at all. I've never been able to understand why the makers put that little bait-peg on them – it gives people the wrong idea from the start.' He expounded his own method, which he said was fool-proof. A rat in a room will at some time during the night run round the whole perimeter of the walls, and an unbaited snap-trap placed with the spring-platform against the wall was therefore infallible. But, he added, all traps became obsolete with the introduction of *Warfarin*, and rodents need no longer present a problem to anybody.

Accident, fire and flood. Dirk the deerhound broke his leg. Any dog with a broken tibia produces many problems; when the dog weighs something like a hundredweight and the leg is the better part of a yard long, the problems are disproportionately increased. It had become a stereotype that after any absence from Camusfeàrna I would inevitably return to find that some disaster had taken place while I was away, and Dirk's accident conformed precisely to that pattern. Lavinia and I had been visiting friends some fifteen sea miles or 120 road miles to the southward; we had travelled by car, and had formed an intricate plan by which both sea and road transport were available for other family projects. My stepson Nicholas and Jimmy Watt had been invited to fish a salmon river the following day, in the area where we had been staying; we therefore decided to leave the car at the fishing port there, where the *Polar Star* had been undergoing some adjustments to her gear-box, and return to Camusfeàrna in her. We could then immediately transport Nicholas and Jimmy to the port by boat, leaving them the use of the car and ourselves returning to Camusfeàrna in the *Polar Star*.

This plan, surprisingly, we carried through without interference by weather or any of the many other factors that might have caused its dislocation, but when we dropped anchor in Camusfeàrna bay to take Nicholas and Jimmy on board, they brought the news that Dirk had broken his leg a few minutes before.

The dog had been in the house when Terry had announced that the *Polar Star* was on the horizon, and the whole party went out to watch her; Dirk, not in those days the best disciplined of dogs, had slipped out unnoticed and set out for a canter on the hill. No one was aware of his absence until a few minutes later, when a newly appointed estate manager who had been inspecting the forestry ground knocked at Camusfeàrna door and announced to Terry: 'Your dog's up there by the hill track, and he seems to have hurt himself pretty badly.'

Terry found Dirk at a distance of something like half a mile from the house, howling pitifully and unable to rise, each successive struggle causing him even intenser agony. It was obvious to Terry that Dirk had a fractured foreleg, and equally obvious to him that there was no way to get the dog home but to carry him, for to construct a stretcher would mean leaving Dirk for a long time in his present plight. It was fortunate that Terry, though past his sixteenth birthday by only four days, was constructed to the same Goliath specification as Dirk; two years at Camusfeàrna had transformed him from a pallid London child into a Hercules of six foot two and thirteen stone. Dirk has never been accurately weighed, but Bell's *The Scottish Deerhound* gives the weight of a dog standing thirty inches at the shoulders as 95 to 105 lb, and Dirk is very considerably over thirty inches. Terry simply picked him up, one hand under his chest and the other under his haunches, and carried him home. He remarked that had the incident taken place five days earlier he would have performed this feat at the age of fifteen.

The vet arrived soon after Lavinia and I had returned from our southward journey with the *Polar Star*, and in half an hour the dog's leg was set and plastered, but we were barely at the beginning of our troubles. Even an able-bodied dog of Dirk's proportions occupies a surprising amount of space in a cottage the size of Camusfeàrna; but only now, immobilised by his injury, did his vast extended frame reveal the enormity of his stature. In broad terms he occupies three feet by five, and the slightest attempt at movement of any kind caused him an agony so acute that he could not contain his voice, so that night and day became hideous with his screams. To move him out of doors so that he might relieve himself was the work of two men, carrying and manoeuvring through doorways his vast forequarters and thereafter supporting him in this helpless position until necessity overcame his inhibitions and he allowed his sphincters to relax. He required constant nursing night and day, and after the first two nights it was clear that we could not keep him at Camusfeàrna throughout his convalescence. We made arrangements for his reception at a hospital kennel in Inverness the following day and addressed ourselves to the problems of his transport. We spent the morning building a stretcher; this we covered with foam rubber cushioning and over it we nailed an army blanket, the free portion of which would be passed over the prostrate dog and in turn nailed down to hold him in position.

It was just after we had succeeded in carrying Dirk from the house and laying him on the stretcher that a party of unannounced visitors arrived. They were, they told Terry, friends of some people whom I had received earlier in the year, and who had told this party that they were sure I would not mind if they called. To the best of my recollection there were five or six of them, a comparatively modest invasion, for families holidaying in the

West Highlands seemed often to consist of double that number. I told Terry to explain that I could not see them at present, but that if they cared to go for a walk and return in an hour it was possible that the present crisis would be over. They did not choose to leave immediately, but stayed to annoy Teko by peering at him over the paling, thus adding his penetrating voice to Dirk's pathetic howls as we arranged his sprawling carcass upon the stretcher.

We manoeuvred the huge wooden structure through the rear door of the Land Rover with the greatest difficulty, for the door itself was narrow, and we had to tip the stretcher at an angle of forty-five degrees before it would pass through and lie flat across the seats. The nailed blanket, however, held Dirk from sliding, and the stretcher settled neatly into its position.

The Land Rover set off very slowly up the steep track. At the end of half an hour it had progressed less than two hundred yards, for the tyres found no grip upon the slippery mud of the steep gradient, and Jimmy and Terry were once more reduced to hauling the car up by her own winch.

At this point the visitors returned; my apologies for inability to receive them after all evoked no other response than unconcealed and boorish anger that they had been sent on a fruitless walk instead of being informed of the fact when they first arrived. The very gaucherie of their egregious presumption deprived me of words. They retired huffily to a neighbouring hilltop, from where they watched with sour satisfaction our struggles with the improvised ambulance.

When at length Jimmy and Terry reached the metalled road their real troubles began. The braking power of the Land Rover being greater than her acceleration, Dirk was perpetually shifted forward and downward on his stretcher; since he could use only his hind limbs in an effort to rise or readjust his position, their pushing movements only propelled him further towards the bulkhead between him and the driving cab. Each one of these movements pressed the strained blanket against his plastered fore-leg. Jimmy remembers the eighty-mile journey as a nightmare, Dirk screaming and helplessly defecating where he lay, so that the stench in the car became almost as unbearable as the pitiful sounds of the dog's distress. A score of times they halted to rearrange him, and by the time they arrived at their distant destination both Dirk and his stretcher were anchored by a spider's web of string and rope to every stable object in the rear of the Land Rover. Accident, fire and flood.

9

Société Anonyme

A FRIEND, with whom I travelled in the autumn of 1962 to Southern Europe and North Africa, had long suspected the existence of an international body whose French branch he knew to bear the title of *Société Anonyme pour la Confusion des Voyageurs*. That there were affiliated or subsidiary organisations all over the world was evident, but the locality of the ultimate H.Q. remained unidentified. During our journey I came to suspect it of being mobile; it was the off season for tourists, and the highest officials of the organisation, who by their very skill could only be attached to H.Q. appeared to be in constant touch with our progress or lack of it.

The new Algerian Cabinet had, in November 1962, a *Caisse d'Equipement*. A *Caisse d'Equipement* for an agent of the *Société Anonyme pour la Confusion des Voyageurs* would at its most basic level contain the following items, to be used at discretion and to create the greatest confusion. A well-trained agent will go far with the following signboards; they are designed specifically to reduce to captivity or lunacy the driver of a motor vehicle, and each *caisse* must be assumed to contain the essentials for one town or village only. The following list for a French-speaking country is deductive, and applies to the off season in summer; when the flow of foreign tourist traffic is greater, and funds derived from fines are ploughed back into the firm, the number of items can be greatly expanded without loss of profits.

a 1 sign *Toutes Directions*
b 8 signs *No Entry* (International Code)

c 4 signs *Défense de Stationer* (1 verbal, 3 International Code)
d 10 signs *Fermé sans Date*
e 10 signs *Tirez* and *Poussez* (to be reversed)
f 4 signs *Hommes* and *Femmes* (to be reversed)

As an example of how the first three items can be employed to the greatest effect by an intelligent agent I cite the following two alternatives; both, clearly, are taught in the primary course of instruction, and both are seen here from the traveller's eye viewpoint.

Upon entering the purlieus of a considerable village or medium-sized town one is surprised to see that the main, the obvious, route to the town's centre is blocked by a *No Entry* sign, while an arrow with the words *Toutes Directions* points to a side-street on the right. This street is straight and narrow and leads into a square. Sometimes the centre of the square is ornamented with an equestrian statue, but always it is made hideous by a huge notice *Défense de Stationer*. A few cars of foreign identity are touring round and round the square in a hesitant, jerky fashion; one, with Swedish number-plates, has run out of petrol, and several gendarmes are gathered round it with notebooks and snarls of triumph. The Swede does not speak French; his wife is in tears. Still unsuspecting, one follows the sparse traffic. Only slowly does it dawn upon one that all exits from this square – let us say five in all – bear No Entry signs, including the street from which one has emerged. *Défense de Stationer*. Round and round the square, hope dying, despair growing, the close press of circulating cars ever increasing, the cruel gloating gaze of the gendarmes following like vultures behind a wounded animal. Time must have a stop, defiance is useless; the car coasts to rest and the vultures close in with their notebooks, their bills, their beaks. Later, they will have the car removed and direct the traveller courteously to an hotel bearing the *Fermé sans Date* notice. (If it is open items (*c*) and (*f*) may be used to advantage, but only after the first quarter of an hour.)

Alternative: the same *Toutes Directions* sign, but this time the diversion is not short and straight into the trap. It begins as a

154

reasonably broad street, and after a hundred yards it turns at right-angles to the left. It grows narrower and turns at right-angles to the right. Then very much narrower still, room for one small car only, and another corner to the left. By this time the walls of the old town are scraping the car's wings, and it is with a sense of enormous relief that one sees ahead the sunlit stone of a spacious square. It is true that one sees simultaneously the familiar *Défense de Stationer*, but one has not yet learned the lesson. Beyond is no exit from the square, and once again the street of emergence carries the No Entry sign. Many gendarmes are gathered gluttonously round a hundred helpless cars. The *tirez* and *poussez* upon the police H.Q. doors have been reversed; there are broken hinges, and broken glass, and *papillons* are being scattered to the limit of vision.

Surprisingly, it is often in the remotest places that the organisation achieves its greatest virtuosity. Once, lost at midnight on desert tracks in southern Morocco – wind, sand and stars – the headlights of my Land Rover showed a distant but unmistakable signpost. Eagerly I approached it and eagerly directed the searchlight beam full upon its legend. It read, quite plainly and without any possibility of doubt, '*A Sodom et Gomorrah*'. For hell's sake I thought, this is the turning-point of sanity. I'm several thousand miles off course, and several thousand years behind time. I got out of the car and investigated the outrage in detail. It was a wooden board, and the paint was quite fresh; near to its foot was a pile of camel dung, also quite fresh.

It was not until several days later that I learned of an American Film company who had tentatively chosen the fantastic desert city of Ait Ben Haddou as the setting for the expenditure of a sum that was phenomenal even by Hollywood standards. Other, as then unrecognised, activities of the organisation came to mind. Approaching the outskirts of Hamburg at 11 p.m. the main oil-feed pipe of my car breaks; I am due at Le Touquet the following day; I speak no German other than that learnt parrotwise in early childhood from German Poetry for Recitation. *Der Alkoenich* and *Der Alte Barbarossa* are inadequate to the present situation.

. . . Entering the Spanish frontier at Irun; despite the fact that one could throw a stone into France, no official speaks one word of French. My Land Rover, heading for North Africa via Gibraltar, contains various firearms including a pistol. From the frontier I am driven in a police car to a police H.Q. in a town some ten miles distant. There is no competent official. When he arrives an hour later there is no interpreter. He appears entirely fortuitously after the competent official has left again. After three hours I am allowed to retain rifle and shot-gun, the case of each now fitted with some sort of chastity belt, but the pistol is confiscated. I may recover it at Algeciras police station in two days' time; it will be there long before I can get there myself by car. I wait a week in Gibraltar and visit Algeciras daily, but no one has heard of the pistol. Through the good graces of an officer of the Gibraltar Garrison I receive it in England, four months later.

My object has been to explain the principle of the organisation before narrating the story of a journey made hideous by its activities.

I left England by car in late November 1961. One of the more childish hobbies that I have carried with me into middle age is the driving of very fast cars, and the year before I had bought a Mercedes-Benz 300 S.L. Roadster. While not appreciably faster than the old converted Grand Prix Maserati that had preceded it, the Mercedes was by contrast, utterly reliable, comfortable and weatherproof. I accorded to this car the feelings conventionally appropriate to the most costly single possession that one has ever owned, and a scratch upon its glossy coachwork disturbed me as much as would a boil upon my own face.

I had business in France, Majorca and Algeria, and our itinerary required a strict time schedule to avoid total disruption. We were to drive from Le Touquet to Barcelona, ship the car to Palma, and fly on there ourselves the following morning. After four days in Majorca we were to fly to Palma – Nice – Algiers, leaving the Mercedes in Palma, spend eight days in Algeria, fly to Algiers – Nice – Palma, and after a further fortnight in Majorca ship the car back to Spain and drive north to various rendezvous in France. The second of the two periods in Majorca I intended to regard as a holiday without responsibility, the first that I had taken for years.

It was pouring with rain when we landed at Le Touquet, and it went on pouring with rain all that afternoon and all the following day. As we drove further south we came into snow and ice; finally, as we left Perpignan, a wind sprang up and increased until it cannot have been less than Force 11 on the Beaufort scale. Zig-zagging down the sea-cliff roads towards the Spanish frontier at Port-Bou the storm plucked and tore at the car until more than once I thought that we should literally be blown off the road and over the edge of the precipice. At the frontier post itself the force of that tearing wind was so great that it took all one's strength to open and close the doors of the car and fight one's way across the road to the frontier buildings.

In Spain it began, inevitably, to rain again, and the windscreen was once more coated with the slush barrage of heavy transport. We arrived in Barcelona after dark, more than an hour after the scheduled time at which the car should have been at the docks.

During my few visits to the country Spanish traffic regulations have remained wholly enigmatic to me; whatever I do or do not do, whistles are blown, accusing fingers pointed, and I am brought to a halt. After some penetrating enquiries the relevance of which is not apparent (for example, the full Christian names of my father, who died in the same year that I was born); after documentary formalities lasting long enough to allow the last hundred laboriously overtaken lorries to repass, I am fined a preposterous sum in hard cash and allowed to set off in dispirited pursuit of the heavy convoys. It must be coincidence that the policeman simultaneously heads for a tavern.

Madrid and Barcelona appear to have given enormous study to the technique of confusion. To a running commentary of chirruping police whistles (sometimes it has seemed to me that these sounds are the true language, the primitive vocalisation of the species, and that human articulation must have been laboriously learned) the packed traffic surges always straight forward, unable to turn left or right or stop without incurring a veritable orchestra of furious chirping.

Thus to say that our entry into Barcelona was filled with frustation would be an understatement; the inexorable flow of traffic, moving to the tune of angry or purely conversational chirps, bore us ruthlessly past every desirable goal. Our immediate destination, I had decided, must be an hotel, from where some employee would accompany us to the shipping company's offices in the town and then direct us to the docks. A simple and eminently sensible programme, but in practice very difficult of achievement. For, although hotels of all types flanked both sides of the long tree-lined avenue down which we swept, any attempt to turn right or left was greeted by the same outraged grass-hopper chorus. There were no *No Entry* signs such as are custo-marily used by the *Société Anonyme*, no *Toutes Directions*; only the relentless, jostling surge of traffic. Caught up in the stream, we were swept onwards, whirled round a great fountain and back down the avenue by which we had arrived.

By some whim of the Society's agent responsible for this street, the whole block of traffic of which we were a unit was suddenly herded off the avenue and right to the doors of the Ritz. This, though clearly disconcerting to some of the cars surrounding us, was the apotheosis of our dreams, and our simple and sensible programme was carried through to the letter.

Meanwhile, however, agents of the Society had been in touch with Palma, finalising the details of our total rout.

The Mercedes had been left at Barcelona dock, complete with her keys, in charge of the shipping company concerned. In exchange for these keys we received the document necessary to reclaim the car at Palma dock on the following day. Euphoria set in.

In the morning we flew from Barcelona to Palma, arriving at the airport a little before midday. As the expensive part of the itinerary still lay ahead of us, we took the airport coach to the town terminus. Entering the outskirts of Palma, and thinking of nothing in particular except that Majorca ought to be warmer in winter, I was amazed to see my own car approaching from the opposite direction. The bus was so high, and the Mercedes so low, that I could see nothing of the driver as he passed; looking back after him I could make out through the rear window of the Mercedes that there was no passenger, and that the head and shoulders of the driver had the contours of a very young man with ruffled hair. Somehow I retained an impression of overalls or dungarees. Then the Mercedes had disappeared round a bend, and our bus continued on its sedate way into Palma.

We did, immediately, jump to conclusions, but we were anxious to give them the benefit of the doubt. Upon arrival in the town we left our luggage in a café and went immediately to the port. The sentry of the port police, clearly a minor employee of the Society, informed us that the port was closed until four p.m. It was then half past one. Neither of us spoke enough Spanish to argue the point with any persuasion.

Resigned by now to passing the day making sport for the organisation, but still unaware of the magnitude of the disaster it had prepared for us, we took a taxi back to the airport. It was just possible, we argued, that some employee of the shipping company had tried to deliver the car to us there. The taxi driver spoke a little French, and when we had explained our predicament he joined enthusiastically in the treasure hunt.

The airport knew nothing of the Mercedes, nor had it at any time visited the premises.

The taxi driver suggested that whether or not the port was officially closed it should be possible, with his local knowledge, to visit the dock office of the shipping company and there to pursue further enquiries. We returned to Palma.

During the drive we speculated as to the probable fate of the car. All the facts pointed to theft, yet they refused to fall into place. A vehicle of the Mercedes's striking, not to say garish, appearance (the body was scarlet, the head white) could not possibly be concealed in an island the size of Majorca, much less removed from it and converted into cash elsewhere. From the start I leaned to the theory that the car had been illicitly borrowed, possibly for a joy ride, by someone whose place of work was inside the docks, and that she would eventually be found abandoned somewhere in the countryside not too far from Palma, for the thief would presumably have to return to the docks by some specific hour. In all these suppositions I proved to be right, but nothing had prepared me for the circumstances in which she was to be found abandoned.

At the dock office of the shipping company the taxi driver was forceful and voluble. An alert-looking young clerk of the company hustled us through the throng and bustle of busy warehouses and finally ran to ground a small, seedy and exceedingly shifty looking Majorcan of some fifty years. Nature had never endowed him with beauty, and now his obvious apprehension did not help to produce a reassuring mien. After two or three minutes of unintelligible Majorcine conversation he produced the ignition key of the Mercedes from his trouser pocket; it required no advanced knowledge of the language to understand that here was the man responsible for guarding the car, and that he had no knowledge at all of its whereabouts. It had disappeared; so much was evident.

At this point we explained to the clerk that we wished to put the matter into the hands of the police. In broad principle he agreed, but urged that we should approach the port police, since it was from the port that the car had disappeared. We concurred, with the reservation that we should also approach the Guardia Civil, since the Mercedes had been last seen, not in the docks, but upon the open road. He brushed this rider aside and led us to the office of the port police. Here a tired looking civil servant informed us that there would be no competent officer on duty for some hours. We returned to our taxi and directed the driver to the Headquarters of the Guardia Civil.

Inside the swing doors at the top of the broad flight of steps the equivalent of a constable sat upon a bench reading the daily paper. We asked to see the officer in charge. Later, perhaps, he said; the officer was having lunch . . . an hour, two hours . . . no, there was no available officer at the moment. My companion, who, though as helpless as I was in Spanish, was completely bilingual in French, exploded. What would happen, he asked with little unction, if there had been a murder or a bank robbery? The constable asked whether there had been in fact a murder or a bank robbery. Finally my companion delivered himself of a summary: 'We wish,' he said, 'to talk to no one else than the Chief of Police for all Majorca. A car of great value, unique in this island, and possibly in all Spain, has been stolen from the docks and is now upon the open roads of Majorca.' The constable began to reply that if it had been stolen from the docks we should address ourselves to the port police, but during the course of my companion's impassioned speech a door had opened, and an officer of unidentified rank had emerged and listened. Something in this speech had evidently touched off a train of ideas, a link, apparently, with something he already knew. He looked thoughtful. Asking us to wait for a few moments, he disappeared into an inner courtyard. We waited for more than a few moments, but eventually he returned and ushered us through the courtyard to a small upstairs office. The taxi driver was allowed to accompany us as interpreter; none of the officers spoke any other language than Spanish.

Upon entering this office the first thing that caught my eye was a portable Olivetti typewriter in a soft case. Olivettis are not rare, but this particular one was either my own or its twin in every respect, even to the staining of the case. Then, as I took in the rest of the room. I became aware that the whole multiple contents of the Mercedes was stacked against one wall – suitcases, cameras, books, tins of engine oil, all that had been crammed into the boot and locked there before the car was shipped from Barcelona.

My first reaction was one of profound relief that the Mercedes had been traced; then almost in the same instant I realised that the exhibits included the tool kit and the tonneau cover. The removal from the car of literally everything that was portable could only mean one thing. Almost simultaneously with the thought I heard the voice of the taxi driver: 'Your car has had an accident, a very bad accident. It is *kaput* – it is not possible to repair it in any way, ever.'

We rallied; we asked who had been driving it. 'It is not known. The remains of the car are now being towed to Palma. The police request you to return here at six o'clock this evening to complete all formalities.'

It was clear that we needed linguistic allies of more official status than the taxi driver. We needed an authorised interpreter and a lawyer. We went to the British Consulate, where we learned that the Consul was confined to bed with *la grippe*. From there we went to the agent of some English friends, and arranged for him and a lawyer of his choice to accompany us to police headquarters at six o'clock.

The four of us were punctual. The police officers present were now of high rank and appeared keenly, if slightly suspiciously, interested in the unfolding of the drama. To set the ball rolling they gave us the bare facts. At a fashionable seaside village some five miles from Palma, the Mercedes, evidently driven at a very great speed, had come into contact with a concrete column, and had been virtually cut in two. What connected the two halves, they added with relish, was bent in the form of a semicircle. Shortly after the accident, which was unwitnessed, a young man had presented himself at a first aid post in the neighbourhood. After treatment for contusions he had asked to go to the lavatory, from which, it was discovered quite a long time later, he had made his exit by the window, never to reappear.

The preparation, translation, and typing of my statement took an interminable time. The introductory paragraph held a note of caution, not to say disbelief. 'The holder of British Passport No. 24022, who claims that his name is Gavin Maxwell, and says that his father was called Aymer and his mother Mary, tells the following story. . . .'

At the close of these lengthy and ponderous proceedings, my companion was mysteriously whisked away by an officer of the flying-squad, dressed entirely in black leather. At the same time it was politely proposed that I should go to inspect the remains of the Mercedes in the garage to which it had been towed. 'Where are they taking him?' I asked the interpreter. 'To the first aid post to see whether it was really he and no other that was the driver of the car. These boys don't leave a lot to chance once they get going.'

We walked to the garage, the Mercedes agent for Palma, where a multilingual foreman greeted us. 'I have seen many fantastic accidents – accidents of all kinds – look,' he pulled an envelope of small photographs from his inside pocket and began to display his fantastic and lifetime-long collection of improbabilities (one was of two saloon Mercedes, of which the larger was parked foursquare on the roof of the smaller; '*he* was killed,' said the foreman, 'very dead'), 'but never I have seen an accident like your car and the driver still alive.'

The description of the Mercedes's condition had been no great exaggeration. The shape of the chassis was such that the car could only have been parked with accuracy upon the circumference of a rather small circle. Only the fact that the car had left-hand drive had saved the driver; just forward of the passenger's seat a great square extending right to the midline of the car had been, as it were, removed *in toto*. Into this space two men could walk in and stand. This was the shape and form of the concrete column that had sunk into her, as violent a bodily rape as could be imagined. There was clearly little worthy of salvage beyond the tyres, and possibly the upholstery. The mystery of the ignition key was explained; the wires had been pulled out from behind the dashboard and connected to each other by hand.

Our destination had been a village on the east side of the island; now we were requested not to leave Palma until further notice.

We stayed at a hotel whose pretentious restaurant printed a multilingual menu, a column in Spanish, another in French, and a third in English. This cheered us slightly, for the English column was headed with an unashamed declaration of cannibalism:

'Our chef suggests *you* today.'

He suggested, among culinary curiosities too numerous to mention:

> *Lamb soup Hodge-Podge*
> *The Short Broth with Egg Joke*
> *Spoked and granished Esturgeon*
> *Froce meat*
> *Balls, Catalonian style*

The following day was entirely occupied by legal formalities. In the evening an urgent telephone message arrived from police headquarters. The thief had been apprehended; would I present myself immediately before he was transferred to prison.

The same office, with my luggage stacked against the wall. Several police officials of steadily augmenting rank. Three-quarter rear view, leaning forward in his chair and holding his hands in his lap because they were handcuffed, sat a very blond and very young man. The interpreter asked me if this was the man whom I had seen driving my car. I moved round until I could see the back of the boy's head silhouetted against the white wall; it was a replica of the momentary image I had retained of the Mercedes driver. I said I could not be certain, but that there was a strong resemblance. The presiding police officer spoke rapid Majorcine; when he had finished the interpreter said: 'The officer says he did not bring you here to identify the boy. They already know that it was he. He asked you to come here so that you might see he had wasted no time in finding and arresting the criminal. And, because he knows that you are a writer and you may sometime write about Spain, he wanted you to see that it was not a Spaniard who had stolen and wrecked your car. This is a north German boy from a cargo ship in the port. He is an orphan and has no near relations. He speaks fluent English, and you may ask him anything you like.'

Disconcerted by the mass presence of police, I said less to the terrified boy than humanity demanded. He said: 'I don't remember what happened. . . . I had been drinking in the morning. . . . I'm very sorry I took your car, and very sorry I can't pay for it. I never meant to steal it, only to have a drive in it. Please believe me I'm very sorry.'

The following morning I had to make a second lengthy deposition, this time to the judiciary authorities. In the course of the preliminaries I learned that Ehrenfried Muller would probably serve four years in prison for the combined charges to be laid against him. 'Does he know this?' I asked. 'I expect so. By now the lawyer employed by the German consul will have told him.' I asked whether the Spanish authorities could charge him with

Above – Mossy, distrustful as always

Below – Monday and Lavinia

Lavinia and Monday

Mossy and Monday. 'They had taken up permanent residence
under the floor of the new wing.'

Lavinia, Dirk and
Monday

Above – Nicholas

Below – Simon

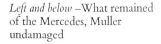

Above – The column (at the near end of the awning) that the Mercedes struck after her *tête à queue* at 100 m.p.h., having entered this photograph from the left

Left and below –What remained of the Mercedes, Muller undamaged

Above – Camusfeàrna, February 1963

Below – The *Polar Star*, April 1963

the theft if I did not, and was told no; his time might thus be reduced to two years. It seemed to me brutal to have any part in such savage sentences upon the follies of youth, and I refused to lay charges that appeared to serve no purpose other than spite.

A few days later I left Majorca for Algiers.

It was not until some time later, after a week spent in Algeria, that I visited the scene of the accident, and failed utterly to reconstruct the circumstances. I had known the name of the village, Campastilla, and that the offside of the car had struck a concrete pillar at a very high speed. I also knew from Muller that he had been driving away from Palma, that the accident had in fact taken place a very few minutes after I had sighted the car.

In my hired SEAT 600 I left Palma with a very clear idea of what I was looking for and a certainty of recognising it when I saw it. It had to be a left-hand bend – whether sharp or merely a long curve made little difference given the speed of which the Mercedes was capable – and somewhere on the right of the roadside there must be a concrete post or column. Campastilla was shown upon the map as a small coastal village, and it did not seem likely that the spot would be difficult to identify.

The approach to Campastilla was dead straight, and there was no concrete pillar anywhere. The village was short, with a detectable left-hand curve, it is true, and when one emerged from it there was the sea on the right-hand side, with no intervening wall or obstacle, and a ribbon development of *plage* hotels on the left. This situation obtained for a further two miles, by which time signboards showed us that by no stretch of the imagination could we be said to be still in Campastilla.

Utterly mystified, we turned the car, drove back to Campastilla and made enquiries. Ten minutes later we were at the site of the disaster. It was a concrete column, one of three or four forming a very short and modest arcade, and various small red relics of the Mercedes were discernible in the dust at its foot. The concrete had been extensively repaired very recently.

All this, however, was on the left-hand side of the road.

The shop behind the column was a small grocery. Through an

obliging interpreter from a nearby hotel we learned all that he knew of the story. He and his wife had been in the back room of the shop, sitting quietly over a glass of wine, when there had been a gigantic crashing noise and the whole building had rocked and shuddered. Running outside he had found a red racing car impaled upon the pillar and facing towards Palma. At the wheel was a half-conscious young foreigner. The grocer gave him brandy and revived him, and then asked whether the driver would like to deposit the luggage from the car in the safety of the shop. The boy had replied hurriedly that the car was not his, and boarded a passing bus.

The grocer pointed out to me that one half of the pillar's width was of sandstone while the other was of reinforced concrete; had the car hit the sandstone portion the column would in all probability have collapsed and carried with it the roof above. Had the car missed the column it must inevitably have entered either his shop or the empty shop next door; in either case the driver must certainly have been cut to pieces by glass.

I had been looking for a concrete pillar on the right hand side of the road; now it transpired that for some unapparent reason the car had performed a complete *tête à queue* in a twenty-five foot width of dry road and had finished by facing in the opposite direction.

Twenty yards, two houses, beyond the site of the accident stood an elegant house upon whose ground-floor balcony a black monkey with a long tail and a jewel-studded collar diligently searched its fur. My interpreter indicated the creature with a pointing finger: 'The mother of that gibbon was looking at the sea – no car passed her vision. Then she heard the impact and she and her monkey run out, and there is a car, making part of the column, but pointing towards Palma. I know well the mother of that monkey; she invents nothing.'

At this juncture the monkey, the mother of the monkey and a small dog of indeterminate breed crossed the road ensemble; the monkey, stepping daintily, held its tail vertically and delicately curled forward over its back. I perceived that the mother of the monkey had no reason to invent anything; an aura of incredibility

166

already surrounded the *ménage;* but they knew all, even though they might remain inscrutable.

'I think,' said the interpreter, 'that the German boy sees the monkey, walking in the road like that, and thinks he sees like pink elephants – so he slams the brakes – from 120 m.p.h., and all the rest happens. But,' he added reflectively, 'it is all like a dream – one does not understand.'

I did not understand. My curiosity was aroused to the pitch at which nothing but Muller's own account of the disaster could satisfy me. Through my lawyer I arranged to see him in prison on the following Saturday, in three days' time.

On arrival at the prison it was plain that the Society was at work again. As I had laid no civil charges against him, Muller had been bought out on bail by the German Consul, forty-eight hours before. The prison authorities did not know his address. My lawyer, who had arranged the visit, was disconcerted but did not accept defeat. 'Now, we go to the court-in-law where haves the address inscribed, and the judge give.' But he did not give.

We went to the law courts. 'The judge's mother is staying mort yesterday; judge gone. Now we go to number two court-in-law.' At the second court, quite a long way away: 'The judge of number two court-in-law is sick at home. Now we go to the *audencia*; there I have much hope. But it is long way – you wait in this café, and I come back ten minutes.'

After three-quarters of an hour he returned triumphantly waving a slip of paper. 'Here is Muller's address – it is in the suburbs, it is better we take a taxi. If he is not in they certainly know at what hour he return.'

We drove a couple of miles out of Palma into a district of surprisingly gracious villas. We found No. 23 without difficulty. An exceedingly suspicious-looking woman opened the door – partially – to the lawyer, and denied all knowledge of any German. When the lawyer returned to the taxi he was visibly ruffled.

'*Not* is possible to understand this,' he said. 'I see with my eyes the address inscribed in the book at the *audencia*. Perhaps the woman she is told say nothing. But *not* I understand. Now we telephone the German Consul.'

It being Saturday there was no answer, and a visit to the Consulate produced only echoes of our knocking at the door. The lawyer was baffled at last. 'Not I can do anything at all before Monday. By one o'clock on Monday I shall telephone you with all arrangements made.'

At one o'clock on Monday he telephoned to tell me that all offices were closed and that nothing was possible until the Christmas season was over on Thursday the 27th. He himself would unfortunately be absent from Palma until the afternoon of Friday 28th, and no official would thereafter be available until the following Monday.

Meanwhile the monkey motif remained curiously strong. Jimmy Watt came to Majorca for a few days of his holiday; we went to the east side of the island, and there, jumping down into the dressing-room of a Roman theatre, he dislocated his ankle. By the time we reached a hotel the swelling was alarming, not so much by virtue of its size as by its extreme distension over a very small area, with very considerable extravasation. I thought that Jimmy should be X-rayed immediately.

We were ashamed to jump the gigantic queue at the clinic – if more than 150 amiably disposed and dispersed persons in the waiting-room and the corridors could be called a queue – but we excused our privilege on linguistic grounds.

The clinic was remarkable, both by its extreme formality and extreme efficiency. The doctors were voluble, human, expert. Everybody watched everybody else being treated; everybody smoked like chimneys, and appeared to expect everybody else to do the same. There was less formality than I have ever seen among official classes in any country. Jimmy's X-ray and diagnosis were performed in record time and a number of well-wishers came forward to talk to him while his bandage was drying. There happened to be a momentary visiting lull when he cocked his ears and said: 'That's a monkey – nothing else makes a noise like that.' I listened and said I thought it was some kind of mechanical toy, like an india-rubber dog that squeaked if you pressed it. Jimmy insisted, and as he was unable to walk himself I volunteered to investigate. The open doorway of the next surgery framed a strange scene. On the operating table sat a young woman who had recently undergone some nasal surgery; her nose was encased in plaster and strapping, from which protruded the ends of two small wooden splints. She was surrounded by a large number of people of all ages and sizes, some three or four of whom were engaged in taking flashlight photographs. On the outskirts of this throng stood a couple of nuns, and from somewhere on the floor, at a point hidden by their voluminous skirts, emanated the strange sounds that had attracted Jimmy's attention. I still leaned to the theory that it was produced by a child with a vocal toy. At that moment one of the nuns stooped and picked up something which she held cradled in her arms as one would hold a very small baby. The noise stopped. I was completely puzzled – no child of a size that could be hidden by the nun's arms could have been left on that foot-crowded floor. Taking advantage of the general policy of *laissez-faire*, I walked into the surgery and stood beside the nun as she bent her head and crooned over whatever it was that she held. A small arm, black and hairy and shiny, reached up from the folds of her drapery and put its hand confidingly round her neck. A moment later she turned, and I was looking into the face of the smallest chimpanzee I had ever seen. Now, a nun cuddling a baby chimpanzee in an operating theatre is an unusual composition, by any criteria, both in *dramatis personae* and in setting. Language difficulties prevented satisfaction of my curiosity from the nun herself, but the doctor attending Jimmy spoke French. When he returned to powder the zinc bandage I asked him, a little timidly perhaps, because I half expected him to say that the whole scene was a figment of my imagination, about the monkey.

'The chimpanzee?' he said. 'It's our mascot. Do you like it? I'll get it for you – wait a minute.' He went out and returned with the chimp; he put it into my arms and it put an arm round my neck and snuggled up to me.

'She came to us in a curious way. A rich man had a son born

to him with club hands; the fingers were not only webbed but there was bone fusion, and to give him working fingers needed a very complicated operation. However, I knew I could do it, and I told the father so, but perhaps I didn't explain clearly enough that it was an operation that could only be done in stages – that I could not give the child ten workable fingers after one operation. Anyway, the child was admitted to the clinic, and I performed the first stage, which was a central division giving him two mobile units on each hand. When the father came back and saw this he supposed it be all that I could do, and he was bitterly disappointed; he lost all confidence in me, and wanted to take the child to another surgeon. I protested that I would make those hands as mobile as a monkey's. He said: "If you really do, I'll give you the most expensive monkey in the world."

'Well, my operation was wholly successful, and he kept his promise; perhaps a baby gorilla would have been more expensive still, but we couldn't really cope with a gorilla here. This little chimpanzee is just two months old; she's affectionate and gentle to everyone and everyone loves her dearly. And she's so healthy because she's looked after by a team of expert doctors. Come my little one, and I'll take you back to your aunt.'

My long-delayed meeting with Muller took place the following week, by the simple expedient of leaving at the German Consulate a message and a proposed rendezvous. Thus our second meeting, at a luxury hotel, was in marked contrast to our first when he had sat handcuffed between his captors.

I realised very soon that from the point of view of illuminating the mystery of the Mercedes crash our meeting would be sterile, for he remembered nothing at all from a few seconds before the accident until he found himself once more aboard his ship with an agonising right shoulder.

He told me everything he remembered, and in the greatest detail, for he was grateful to me for making possible his release from indefinite detention in a cell of some thirty hardened criminals. He also told me something of his history. His family had been landed proprietors in what is now East Germany; his father had been killed during the war against Russia, and his mother had escaped to West Germany. When he was fourteen years old she had died of cancer and he was entrusted to the care of an uncle; between him and this man there had long existed a marked mutual antipathy. He was sent to sea before his sixteenth birthday, the first time as galley boy and greaser's assistant in a small coaster. Since then he had changed ships many times, and at the date of his arrest he had been an apprentice third officer learning astronomical navigation. By this time he had visited nearly every port in the world, and had acquired something of the orphan sailor's predatory attitude towards life.

He had been drinking a little in the morning of the day in question but he did not think he had been more than very slightly drunk.

He had come ashore shortly before midday, meaning to walk into the town in search of diversion. As soon as he had passed through the dockyard buildings he saw the Mercedes standing glistening at the roadside. He was a car enthusiast, with considerable mechanical knowledge, and had even owned an elderly Mercedes himself. (He had crashed it.) A 300 S.L. was the apotheosis of his dreams; he had not seen more than a score or so in his life, and had fastened longing eyes upon all of them. At first he had no thought other than to admire this splendid toy. He walked round it and studied it from all angles. At length he decided that the owner could not really object to his sitting in the driving seat and indulging in five minutes' fantasy. (Those were his actual words.) He tried the door and found it unlocked.

As he sat at the wheel and felt the controls the open road seemed to stretch away in front of him; he seemed to see the speedometer needle soaring towards 150 m.p.h., to hear the roar of the exhaust in his ears as the car rocketed forward in response to his throttle foot. For some minutes he was lost in a day dream.

It was the hour of siesta, and the port seemed utterly deserted. He could also see for a long way to each side of him. He did not try to pretend to himself that the owner would not mind his taking the car for an hour's drive; the temptation was so great that he did not even ponder to consider the near-certainty of being caught in an island the size of Majorca where such cars are extremely *rarae aves*.

Having made up his mind he worked quickly and skilfully. He pulled out the wires from the back of the ignition switch and began to make a junction. He received several electric shocks, but in his excitement hardly noticed them. His first junction produced an alarmingly loud whine from the fuel injectors, so he was quick to make the second, and the engine started at once.

He had no idea how he was going to get past the port sentries if he was challenged; he had that mentality. They stepped forward, indeed, but seeing an obvious young German in a German car they did not ask him to stop. He was past the first obstacle. For the first mile he was in traffic, and he drove slowly as he had been driving when I saw him from the airport bus. Then he was in the suburbs and began to drive fast, then on an open country road straight but narrow; he remembered that here he was doing between 120–130 m.p.h. Then he entered a deserted village street, and thought that he did not slacken speed appreciably. 'Then I received some kind of terrible mental shock. I don't remember anything more till I was back on the ship. Perhaps a child ran across the road – something like that.'

'No,' I said, 'there was no child. No human being of any description saw the accident.'

After that he only knew what he had been told. Someone took him to a first aid post and examined his torso for broken bones. He had gone to the lavatory and escaped through the window, but he did not remember that either. A man on a motor-cycle, a civilian, had followed him and brought him back. He had returned to his ship in an ambulance; he had no recollection of this, but remembered finding himself aboard with an agonising pain in his right shoulder, greeting his shipmates with exaggerated *bonhomie*.

Later there had been an identification parade. Not knowing that he had been stripped at the first aid post he had not realised the absolute certainty of identification – he had a large brown birthmark on his left breast. When he saw his shipmates asked to open their shirts he gave himself up.

With the hope of shaking his amnesia by trauma, I asked if he would come with me to the site of the accident. As we drove out through the suburbs I noted that he remembered every detail. 'Here I passed a Cadillac', or 'Here in this bit I began to go fast, to use the car's acceleration, which was even more than I had expected it to be', and 'Here the road was quite clear and I began to race'. As we entered the village of Campastilla he said: 'This I remember, but I don't remember the road beyond it. Is it straight?'

'It is,' I replied, 'but you never got there.'

The long curve that formed the end of the village was a little more abrupt than I had remembered it. In the middle of this curve he gave a sudden exclamation. '*Here* something happened, I know it, things seem to be going round like they must have been that day.' I looked at him and saw that he had gone suddenly white. I waited, but whatever had caused that moment of blind panic would not break through to consciousness. 'It's no use,' he said finally, 'it was something terrible like the end of the world, but I don't know what it was.'

So we had to reconstruct the picture by circumstantial evidence. We got out and walked forward. Where the houses came to an end on the right-hand side the sea began. The road had been built up from the sand, so that its seaward side, unprotected, dropped three feet sheer to the beach; twenty yards beyond the houses a part of the retaining buttress had sunk and left a depression some five inches deep and a yard across. Now I understood for the first time exactly what had happened.

As he had said, Muller had reduced speed very little upon entering the village and must have taken the gentle left-hand curve of the street at a full hundred miles per hour. The maximum pull to the right had thus coincided precisely with this hole at the extreme edge of the road, and the shock had thrown the offside front wheel to within inches of the drop. He must have panicked and braked hard while wrenching the steering-wheel to the left; this had started a slide which, when it became broadside, actually swung the rear wheels of the car out over nothing. Only the front wheels, on left lock, remained upon the road, travelling sideways at some ninety miles an hour. When the rear wheels regained terra firma a complete *tête à queue* was thus inevitable. The only remaining mystery was the fantastic chain of coincidences by which in this potentially holocaustic smash, no human being had suffered so much as a broken limb. It was as though the streets had been specially cleared and the reinforced-concrete column placed with a watchmaker's precision, at the one and only point where it could avert disaster.

'I think I have a charmed life,' said Muller. 'It has always been like this, that something has happened to save me. So much so that sometimes when I have thought of killing myself because the world is so bloody I have been stopped by the idea that it was impossible, and so not worth while trying. The first time was when I was four years old, and playing with another little boy on a farm. I fell down a sort of well, only it wasn't water but a tank of cow's urine. I couldn't swim at all, and this tank was enormous, with sheer sides. They told me afterwards that in the whole tank there was one, just one, little stanchion, or it may have been the end of a pipe, an inch or two below the surface. And I'd fallen in just at that point, so my hands found it at once, and I was able to hang on to it for a long time until I was rescued.

'Then when I was about seven or eight, there happened something even stranger. It was a very, very cold winter. On the way home from school there was a frozen lake, not a very big one, but perhaps a hundred yards across. Over most of it the ice was several inches thick, and we used to cross it with a run and as long a slide as we could make – everyone was always trying to see if they could get right across in one slide. There was only one dangerous place, a patch where a spring came up and the water was barely frozen. Well, one day I did a really wonderful slide, but I'd got the direction just wrong, and I went slap into this patch at high speed. The ice was as thin as paper, and I went straight into it and straight on under the thick ice beyond it. Now there was only one other place where there was little or no ice, a little patch where, for one hour a day only, the waste from the village houses ran in and thawed it. Well, get this – I went in at one hole in the ice and shot along under its surface for a dozen

174

yards or so and popped up through this other hole, all in a matter of seconds. At any other time of day there wouldn't have been another hole. There have been a hundred things like that in my life; it would take too long to tell you them all. But the last two have been perhaps the strangest. Last year in Cuba a man in a port tavern wanted me to sell my watch; he became a nuisance, and I told him to f—— off. He got very angry and said no one could speak to him like that, and he pulled out a big automatic – a Colt .45 I think it was – and pointed it at my head. I thought I could see that the safety-catch was on, so I made a grab for it. But the safety-catch was not on, and he fired, and – look – the bullet went through the top of my left ear.' (He had very small ears, lying flush with the skull.) 'Just the difference of half an inch and it would have killed me, and your Mercedes wouldn't have been crashed by a crazy boy.'

If Muller had been unable to throw any clear light upon his crash he was able to contribute to the records of the *Société Anonyme* the story of its finest hour, the tale of a display of pure virtuosity achieved without any *caisse d'équipement*, without diversion of route or collaboration of recognised officialdom. Some prosperous German acquaintances of his had spent their summer holiday touring Italy in a large new Mercedes-Benz saloon. The party consisted of husband, wife and young children; the luggage, designed to meet every social occasion, had been comprehensive, including much jewellery and costly evening dresses. The family had arrived at the Leaning Tower of Pisa early one Sunday morning, planning thus to avoid a rush of international tourism, and had left their locked car at the foot of the tower from whose cock-eyed summit they surveyed an as yet unawakened world beneath them. The arrival of a breakdown lorry in the car park, a lorry equipped with a heavy crane for lifting cars on to its float, was therefore of some considerable surprise to them, but as yet no subject for anything but idle speculation. Then before, or rather below, their at first unbelieving and then outraged eyes, this lorry positioned itself beside their car, slipped chain slings around its tyres, hoisted it bodily aboard the float, and scuttled rapidly away. By the time the near-hysterical German family had reached ground-level and emerged from the tower there was no sign of lorry or car, nor did they ever recover one single item of all their lost possessions.

'So you see,' said Muller. 'I'm only an amateur really.'

Balls – Catalonian style.

In the end he was charged only with driving without documents, and received sentence of two months and two days, totally remitted for good conduct and character while on bail. He had, however, already served thirty ineradicable days in a provincial Spanish prison.

10

The Tides Return

WHEN at last I had completed the interminable formalities connected with the loss of the car and was able to return to Camusfeàrna I found much change. The house now had many of the amenities of civilisation, including sanitation, a bath and showers, and the tiny kitchen was now all-electric. Every one of these innovations dependent upon water was, however, functionless, for at the date of my return the supply had been frozen for more than a month, and remains frozen at the time of writing five weeks later.

My arrival at the house had a curious, almost surrealistic flavour. During my absence a jeep had been added to the Camusfeàrna transport fleet, and in this we bucked and jolted in the dark down the frozen track whose mud mountains and ruts had become as hard as rock. At the house the headlights showed a single greylag goose standing outside the door, and Jimmy explained to me that of the five that we had imported in the late summer to replace those that had left us in July this was the sole survivor. Two had disappeared only a week ago, fallen prey, probably, to foxes or wild cats whose more usual sources of food supply were cut off by the snow and the cold. Now this single goose tried to push past us into the house, and having succeeded in entering the living-room, tried immediately to jump up on to the sofa whose entire surface was occupied by the sprawling form of Dirk the deerhound. Deterred from this enterprise by Dirk's uncooperative spirit, the goose then hopped into an armchair. At no time in the past had the bird even tried to enter the house. We removed it to the bathroom, and Jimmy had just remarked that despite all the many inconveniences of the month-long freeze we could at least be thankful that there had never been even the briefest power cut, when all the lights went off. We had very little coal, very little paraffin, and no cut wood.

Thus it was sitting in overcoats by candlelight in the freezing living-room that I learned in detail of recent happenings at Camusfeàrna, happenings of which I had heard only in the barest outline.

Terry Nutkins had left Camusfeàrna to become a Zoo keeper in London, and Jimmy was now in sole charge of an increasingly complicated *ménage*.

A few weeks before, a mate for Teko had arrived from Griqualand in South-East Africa. This otter proved to be an enormous animal, bigger than Teko himself, extremely domesticated and affectionate towards human beings, and her introduction to Teko had presented none of the problems we had anticipated. Placed in accommodation adjoining his, so that they might become accustomed to each other's voices and smells before closer acquaintance, she had brushed aside these formalities by climbing into his enclosure during the night, and in the morning they were curled up together in his bed. This happy and promising situation was cut short by her sudden and then unexplained death only two days before my homecoming. She had been healthy and in high spirits in the evening, and when Jimmy had gone in to her in the morning he had found her dead but still perceptibly warm, curled up in Teko's bed under the infra-red lamp, the tip of her tail in her mouth as though she had been sucking it – a habit, like that of Edal sucking her bib, that she had in life.

During the short weeks of her life with Teko, Mossy and Monday had discovered their unrivalled powers of escape from any enclosure in which they might be confined, and on more than one occasion all four animals had been found together in Teko's pool. It would, perhaps be truer to say that Monday had discovered her powers of escape and had somehow coerced her moronic consort into cooperation in such matters as combining their strength to move heavy stones and taking alternate shifts in digging the long tunnels that she planned. Even then, owing to his greater size and absolute absence of initiative, Mossy often found himself left behind while she made her escape through some aperture too small to permit his passage. On this first evening of my return he was alone in the enclosure, but during the night she returned for him and from outside enlarged her latest tunnel until he could squeeze through. From then on, for the first three weeks of my stay, their capture and recapture became our major preoccupation, until at length I was forced to realise that nothing but a zoo cage could confine her, and I accepted defeat.

Monday could climb like a monkey, balance like a tight-rope walker, dig like a badger, move stones that were heavy to a human, jump like a squirrel, make herself thin as an eel or flat as a flounder; no device nor ingenuity of ours could make her once relent her first avowed intent to be a pilgrim. But most of all it was her brain, the systematic application of her many skills and her single-minded pertinacity, that convinced me of the uselessness of the struggle.

She had tasted freedom and she would have no more of prison. It was not, in the prevailing circumstances, an inviting prison or one calculated to lead to resignation; the glass tank frozen, all running water stopped, the small patch of ground now hard as rock and without vegetation. Outside were the sea and the islands with their many habitable lairs among the rocks and the bracken and the rooty heather; outside was the freedom of the waves and the white sands and the weedy rock pools. There was nothing I wanted more than to let her go free, but with the knowledge of all the other tame otters that because of their confidence in man had been shot or bludgeoned to death by the first strange human being they approached, I felt that I must confine her. It took three weeks to convince me that this was not only an impossibility but would be more cruel than any death she could meet in freedom.

One wall of their enclosure was formed by the Camusfeàrna house itself; the other three were of continuous, smooth, wooden paling five feet high. The only points at which the woodwork did present a completely smooth face were the right-angles formed by their own house, of the same height as the paling, and a further right-angle where a heavy straining-post had been boarded round. At the base of the fence we had sunk fine-mesh wire-netting into the ground, extending six inches vertically into the ground and then two and a half feet horizontally inwards. As a further safeguard against tunnelling, we had placed heavy stones along the greater part of the perimeter. This was the prison from which, during a time of bitter frost when the ground was frozen as hard as iron four feet underground, Monday escaped time and again with contemptuous ease.

At the beginning I thought naïvely that our only problem was to catch them, for I could not seriously believe in the impossibility of making the enclosure proof against escape. We constructed in the paling a foot-square drop-hatch that could be closed by the release of a string from an upper-storey window. I disposed a number of eels temptingly a yard or two inside the trap, and at dusk I sat down with the release-string in my hand to await developments. The otters arrived very soon after dark; they came and went between the eels and the hatch so that there was never a clear moment when both of them were inside simultaneously. Eventually I decided that to catch one was better than to catch neither, and I released the string when only Mossy was in the enclosure. I felt certain that Monday would come in to him during the night; in this I was right, but at the time I did not know that she would as certainly perform a rescue, and contrive somehow to extract her clottish companion from captivity before dawn.

During the night I could hear her whistling impatiently to him from outside and his peevish and fretful responses as he explained the patent impossibility of reaching her; at some time in the small hours these sounds ceased, and in my innocence I imagined her to have joined him in their house and settled down for the night.

In the morning they had both gone. She had indeed climbed into the enclosure, but only in order to move a few massive stones, tunnel under the wire-netting and liberate the captive.

The following night, having as I thought made all tunnelling projects impossible, I reset the trap and again sat at the window with the string in my hand. This time I had to wait much longer and it was Monday that I caught. The front door of the house, in temporary disuse, led directly into the enclosure, and I went out to her carrying peace offerings. She ran straight up to me, emitted a breathy, explosive sound of challenge, and gave my boot a sharp, symbolic nip. She then ran to the corner where the paling formed a convex right-angle, and began to shin rapidly up it with the powerful hunching movements of a bear climbing a tree. I had literally to push her down, while Jimmy ran for materials wherewith to form an unscaleable overhang at the top of this corner. In the end it looked as if it would challenge even a monkey's capacities.

The next morning she had gone again. I attached pieces of slippery Formica to the paling at the points where she was wont to climb. Miraculously they gave her no pause. Every night she came brazenly into the trap, insolently confident of her ability to overcome or undermine any obstacle that I might set in the way of her escape before morning. Every day my preparations became more elaborate, and every day she mocked me. The trap was by this time automatic; an ingenious system of strings ensured that when she pulled at eels the hatch would close itself and at the same time ring the ship's bell upon the gatepost. The whole of the area on which she had exercised her feats of climbing was covered by a great sheet of smooth metal, a relic of Teko's first ill-fated pool, and the night after the appearance of this fresh puzzle we caught both Mossy and Monday. They were still there in the morning, and all the day through they slept in their house. I had no doubt in my mind that they were now captive for as long as we wished them to remain so. Twenty-four hours later they had once more vanished, this time by an ambitious tunnelling scheme that involved the moving of a stone weighing some sixty or seventy pounds.

We made only one more attempt. The following evening, just before dusk, Jimmy called to me that Monday had come in through the door of our new extension building and that he had closed it behind her. She came through into the living-room and began to explore, briskly and impatiently, ignoring us altogether, rather in the manner of a testy colonel inspecting company lines. Having exhausted the possibilities of floor-level she moved upwards, displaying a degree of acrobatic power that appeared hardly credible. In the same way that water finds its way downward between and around all obstacles by force of gravity, so she appeared to be borne upward by some like but contrary force concealed within her. High on the shelves she stepped daintily and gracefully amongst the bottles and tins and groceries; finding little to her liking, she returned to the floor with the same sinuously effortless movements, climbed on to the sofa and said something exceedingly rude to Dirk, and finally moved off to continue her researches in the new wing. When she entered the bathroom we closed the door behind her, intending to confine her there until we had secured Mossy. It was a sliding door; in less than three minutes she had discovered the principle of its operation and was back in the living-room.

We coaxed her back into the bathroom and this time secured the door so that there was no means of opening it.

Mossy did not return that night, and in the morning we found that Monday had chewed her way through the bathroom plasterboarding and had already got to work on the woodwork that lay beyond it. She was, however, still captive against her will, and for the first time.

In the evening we caught Mossy, and brought Monday through to join him in their enclosure, which I believed to be now proof against any attempt at escape. During the night there was much whistling and the sounds of heavy stones being moved; at dawn I looked out from my window and saw Monday doing a high rope-walk along the top of the paling. She had not climbed up from inside, but had contrived her escape at ground-level and was now returning for her consort. In a further five minutes they were both on their way to the sea.

It was at this point that I abandoned the struggle, as much on humanitarian grounds as in the knowledge that by one means or another she would always outwit me. I hoped, but with little conviction, that Mossy and Monday would remain in the vicinity of Camusfeàrna and its islands, where they would be at least relatively safe from death at human hands. It was not until several days later, and after Lavinia had joined me from London, that I discovered how little grudge they appeared to bear us for our determination to make them captive, for they had taken up permanent residence under the floor of the new wing.

Their entry to this improbable refuge was under the door that now formed the principal entrance to the house; here immediately below the threshold, was a small unboarded portion giving access to the space between floor and foundations. From this slit, some two feet long and four inches high, Lavinia found that she could call them at will to take food from her hand. The slit was divided in the middle by an upright plank; invariably at her call the two small faces, one blunt and one sharp, would peer out as though from letter boxes, and invariably it would be Mossy who was to the left of the upright and Monday to the right. This position they would assume at the first sound of her calling voice, and they remained completely indifferent to the tramp of human feet stepping over them to enter or leave the house.

Now that their freedom was established, it seemed to me that to encourage this unexpected domesticity we should take every possible step to make their self-selected quarters as luxurious as possible. Choosing a time at which they were both engaged with Lavinia outside, we cut a rectangle in the wooden floor of the room beneath which they had chosen to set up house, and sunk between it and the foundations a well-bedded and draughtproof kennel whose roof was formed by a raisable hatch in the floor of the room. This, to my surprise, they took possession of immediately, but they did not accord a like approval to other arrangements we had made for their comfort. With the idea of protecting them from the prevailing sea-winds we had built up earthworks that covered all the seaward-facing space between the new wooden wing and its foundations, thus leaving the otters only one common entrance and exit. We had forgotten an otter's insistence upon alternativ means of egress; the next morning the earthworks had be efficiently tunnelled in two different places. The amount of labour that they had put into this work was, however, an encouragement to believe that they considered themselves to be perfecting otherwise ideal and permanent quarters.

At morning and before dusk they would, as I have said, come out to Lavinia's call and take food from her hand, but as to where they went at night we had no knowledge until she followed them. It was a season of bitter cold; the days were for the most part still and bright with winter sunshine, but the nights were arctic, and the burn was frozen right down into its tidal reaches, with a layer of ice that capsized as the tide went out and floated up to form a new and thicker layer as it returned. A little before dusk one evening Lavinia, who had been down to the burn to break the ice and draw water, heard them calling to each other at some little distance from the house. Following Monday's small, urgent voice, she came upon them playing in a partly frozen pool, shooting under stretches of ice, and bobbing up where it ended, climbing on to it and rolling upon it, diving back and splashing as they sported together. Fearing that they would resent her intrusion, and read into it some further attempt at capture, Lavinia had approached them by stealth, crawling upon all fours; only when they began to move on down the stream did she stand up and call to them, but they found in her presence no cause for any alarm. As they neared the tide she walked beside them, their heads now no more than silhouettes on a sea blanched by sunset colours, until suddenly a curlew rose before them with its rasping cry of warning, and in a panic they turned and raced back upstream and into the darkness. The next night again she followed them down the burn in the dusk, and lost them in the thickening darkness as they swam out towards the islands.

With the liberation of Mossy and Monday, something seemed to me restored to Camusfeàrna, something that had been lost for many months, for once again these were wild creatures free without fear of man and choosing to make their homes with him. As if to reinforce this mood, two of the wild geese suddenly returned after an absence of seven months; one of them was the great gander who had sired all the young of the previous year, and now on the very day of his arrival came straight up to us to take food from our hands. Somehow, with all this unwary confidence in mankind he had survived the autumn and the winter months and fallen prey to no wildfowler's gun; perhaps he had joined some vast flock of wild grey geese and during his long absence from Camusfeàrna had taken his reactions from them. It is sad that for the otters there is no such safety in numbers; sad to think that Monday's whole dynamic personality may be blotted out to appease momentarily the inner emptiness and frustration that causes the desire to kill.

Before me is a letter from Norway, telling of yet another pet otter done to death.

She was tame and she would follow me like a dog. The last days we used to go fishing in a nearby loch. She jumped about in the rowboat while I was pulling the oars. Now and again I left her alone in the loch, sure to pick her up again when I wanted her to stay at home. But this very morning a mason passing the loch on his way to work saw the kind and confident animal and gave her a kick with his heavy boot. I found her dead, resting on a pile of branches out in the water.

Destruction, empty and purposeless, unmitigated even by the strange intimacy that binds the archetypal hunter to his quarry. I hope that if ever again I write of Camusfeàrna the murder of Mossy and Monday may not mar the pages of my book.

Cascades from our far distant mountain spring
Are scattered into spume by hurricane,
And the sweet vivid stains of childhood clinging
Are blanched from the brightness of their beginning
Into a conform of khaki. All that remain
Become elusive as a woodcock's wing
In autumn dusk. But still the bird of passage
Carries some undelivered, unsigned message,
Some testament, some favourable will;
And with this knowledge I pursued him as a hunter,
Though fleeing like him from some ancestral winter
– Believing that to inherit I must kill.

In bright oases of the desert south
Brown men eat the living hoopoe's heart,
Feeling the muscles pulse inside the mouth.
Only this death can give them back their youth,
Only this blood restore their childhood sight
And bring them knowledge of forgotten truth.
Hunter and hunted too near now, pursuer
Sensing his true role, rejected wooer,
Must kill what he cannot possess;
Knowledge of my true intent, destruction,
Hold me now in counter-poised inaction
And let my lover, bird of passage, pass.